# A MAN OF DISTINCTION

G000113092

It was five years since Anna had, briefly, met Marcus Trent and made such a fool of herself—and she had never seen him since. But now, out of the blue, he had turned up again. Surely he couldn't be bothered about that old story now? But he could, and he did!

*Books you will enjoy*
*by JENETH MURREY*

**THE ROAD TO FOREVER**

For six years Lallie had been in disgrace with her family in general and her bossy stepbrother Owen in particular—and none of it had been her fault, though Owen refused to believe that! Now he had suddenly turned up again, demanding that she come home with him to Wales— and, to add insult to injury, that she should pretend to be engaged to him! Did he really imagine she was going to obey him, just like that?

**THE DAUGHTER OF NIGHT**

Since her mother had abandoned her at birth and had since married a very rich man, and since her beloved foster-mother needed money, Hester hadn't had any compunction in demanding that money from her mother. It seemed only justice. But the formidable Demetrios Thalassis took a very different view of the situation and he proceeded to act accordingly . . .

**FORSAKING ALL OTHER**

For three years after their brief and disastrous marriage Alex hadn't set eyes on her husband Greg; indeed, she had hardly given him a thought. But now he had suddenly reappeared, announcing that he wanted her back. Why— when he didn't care any more about her than she did about him?

**TAME A PROUD HEART**

Roz was having problems with her brother-in-law Stephen—so her old friend Charles Maine suggested that one way of keeping him at bay was to get herself involved with another man: himself. But how could Roz take Charles away from his devoted Marjery?

# A MAN OF DISTINCTION

BY
JENETH MURREY

MILLS & BOON LIMITED
15–16 BROOK'S MEWS
LONDON W1A 1DR

*First published 1984*
*Australian copyright 1984*
*Philippine copyright 1984*
*This edition 1984*

© Jeneth Murrey 1984

ISBN 0 263 74755 7

*Set in 10 on 12 pt. Linotron Times*
*07-0384 – 55000*

*Photoset by Rowland Phototypesetting Ltd*
*Bury St Edmunds, Suffolk*
*Made and printed in Great Britain by*
*Richard Clay (The Chaucer Press) Ltd,*
*Bungay, Suffolk*

# CHAPTER ONE

ANNA GENTRY carefully schooled her face so that the little flicker of distaste, which she couldn't hide completely, didn't show. Although, as she afterwards told herself, it hardly mattered. The last thing Philip Carew was looking at was her face, so she could let any emotion she felt cross it, he wouldn't even notice—he was much too deeply involved with his own thoughts, reasons and explanations. However, as soon as he showed signs of finishing his rambling and involved speech, she interrupted.

'I don't think I quite understand, Philip.' She didn't look at him but busied herself with the fat brown teapot and the thick kitchenware cups. 'And as it's a purely private matter between you and my sister, I don't think you should be talking to me about it. It's not my business and I don't wish to become involved between husband and wife—I could be accused of taking sides. Besides, everything being equal, if I'm going to take anybody's side, it's more than likely I shall take my sister's.'

Philip stirred a lot of sugar into his tea and frowned at his teaspoon. His fair complexion had flushed a bit at her reproof and his blunt, good-looking features registered incomprehension as he sought for another way to get his point across.

'It's quite simple, Anna,' he spoke as to a mentally retarded child. 'Isabel's filed for divorce—I received the papers this morning—and of course I've talked the

5

whole thing over with Mother. I can't stop Isa, but I'm determined she shan't have Peggy. If I marry—that is, if I have plans to marry, I shall be in a very strong position to apply for custody of my daughter, a much better position than Isabel will have to show—she can't even give the child a settled home! For all she says—her marvellous tales of possible success, making a name for herself and all that—she has precious little to show for it so far.'

'But don't you think you're being a bit premature?' Anna regarded him dispassionately, taking in his well cut breeches, his upper-bracket hacking jacket, the pale yellow polo-necked sweater and the high polish on his riding boots. She wondered, and not for the first time, why just for once he couldn't let his image slip. He was quite a successful trainer of horses, the stables he ran were well known and well thought of, but did he always have to look as though he'd just dismounted from a spirited hunter? Especially when he was driving a car!

'I like to have everything in order.' Philip went into his explanations again, and Anna groaned inwardly while she thanked the fates that this was Saturday morning and there was no rush to get to work. Any other morning and she'd have been late! '. . . a plan of campaign, a well thought out schedule,' Philip was smiling at her as though her obtuseness was forgiveable, even if he couldn't understand it himself. 'That's the way I've always worked, and I find it pays off in the end.'

Anna shrugged. 'But people and horses—they're not the same thing. Personally, I think you're rushing things. After all, you know what Isa's like, it's quite possible she'll change her mind. She often does things like that, so wouldn't it be better to wait until the whole thing's finalised before you start making plans to remarry? It's not only premature,' she added in a chilly little voice, 'I think it's also in rather bad taste.' She wrinkled her nose as though there was a bad smell somewhere. 'Honestly, Philip, you may have this thing about forward planning, but delicacy you have not!'

'Now, don't be coy, Anna.' She might have been a recalcitrant filly for all the notice he paid to her objections. He'd put on his 'come along and let's have no more of this nonsense' voice. And if she *had* been a filly, she thought he would have slipped the bit between her teeth and added a running martingale for extra security while he patted her flanks. 'After all,' he smiled at her confidently, 'it's what we planned, what we originally intended, isn't it? You and me getting married.'

'*Me?*' The word escaped her lips in an explosion of sound. 'Are you saying that I'm to be the next Mrs Philip Carew—that that's what all this is about? Because if so, let me tell you, you're out of your mind! Our little love affair ended five years ago when you married my sister. It's as dead as the dodo—dead and forgotten!'

'Not by me,' Philip smiled at her winningly. 'I made a mistake when I married Isa, I was swept off my feet by a beautiful face. It was the biggest mistake I ever made, and I'm man enough to admit it.'

Anna gazed at him with horror in her eyes, but at the sight of his smile, the horror turned to exasperation. 'Then for heaven's sake,' she said acidly, 'be man enough to take my "no" for an answer. I know you've admitted a mistake, but now you're saying the mistake you made was mistaken . . . Oh lord, you've got me bogged down! Let me put it simply, as I see it. We were once engaged—you ditched me to marry my sister and I got over it—end of story. And that reminds me, Isa's coming this weekend, so you'd better go before she arrives.'

'Wise Anna.' Philip looked at her fondly and she groaned soundlessly. He'd not listened to a word she'd said! The head under his rough fair hair was full of his master plan, it occupied all his tiny mind, and there was nothing to spare for anything anybody else said or thought. If she needed proof she was right in her thinking, he gave it to her.

'Quite right, Anna. I'll go straight away. We don't want Isa to know what we're up to, do we?'

'What *you*'re up to, you mean. Leave me out of it.' But as she said it, she knew it wasn't registering and she became fascinated by his lack of understanding. Maybe it had something to do with his being so closely associated with horses; animals which she didn't much care for. Alphonse, her standard white poodle, had more intelligence in his tail than the entire contents of Philip's stables had in their collective heads!

With an aggravated sigh, Anna watched Philip go and then carried the tea-things across to the sink where she washed up methodically, and while she was doing this, she managed to block off the portion of her mind which dealt with Philip and concentrated on feeling pleased that the house was bright and fresh, that a proper tea was laid ready for Isa in the small sitting room and that she would have time to change her clothes before her sister arrived.

Isa had said she was bringing a surprise—at least that was what she had written on the card—and Anna went through to the sitting-room to look at all Isa's other surprise gifts. Photographs of Isa—in a supporting role in a Shakespeare play, in supporting roles in modern plays and in supporting roles in television dramas. It was all a bit overpowering, but who was she, Anna, to complain? Isa was absurdly generous about her gifts—each frame was of hallmarked silver! But if there were to be many more of these surprise gifts, they would have to overflow into the drawing-room.

Anna took a quick shower, changing from jeans and tee-shirt—which she wore for housework and gardening—into a slim grey skirt and a pale green silk shirt, and pushed her nylon-clad feet into green high-heeled pumps. Her face, she mused fretfully, needed a bit of attention and she wished she had the strength of mind to get her hair cut. No, she grinned widely at her reflection in the dressingtable mirror, it wasn't strength of mind she needed, it was a whole new head of hair. If her long, silky but dead straight hair was cut short, she would need a perm to keep it tidy, and perms made her head look like an untidy, pale marmalade dishmop—she had tried one when she had first started work and it hadn't been a success.

With a sigh, she brushed her hair until it shone and then coiled it with the expertise of long practice into a knot in the nape of her neck, which she secured with several hairpins. Now for her face, which was just as awkward as her hair. The features were good, taken one at a time—large grey-green eyes set between thick, long, dark lashes and under equally dark, arching brows, a small, straight nose, a rather wide mouth with quite a nice curve to it and a smoothly rounded chin, firm but not obstinate. But when the features were added up, in Anna's opinion, the total effect was commonplace. If only she could have been a raving beauty like Isa!

But she wasn't—which wasn't surprising really since,

although she and Isa had always called themselves sisters, had always thought of themselves as such, there was no real family tie between them at all. When Anna's father had married for the second time, the new Mrs Gentry had come complete with a ten-year-old daughter—a beautiful daughter, and that was that. Five-year-old Anna had welcomed Isa and they'd always got on together, often being more like sisters than the real thing, but Anna often wondered why Isa had to be so devastatingly good-looking, have such golden hair when her own only just escaped being ginger—why Isa had to have such beautiful blue eyes when her own were an almost colourless grey-green.

With a shrug, she smeared a little foundation on her face, flicked a powder puff about a bit and added a touch of lipstick before she went downstairs to finish the dusting which the advent of Philip had interrupted. From the sitting-room window she saw the car come to a halt outside the door, an opulent-looking Mercedes, and watched as the man emerged from the driver's door to go round the vehicle and open the passenger door for Isa to get out.

For the first time in over a year she felt the awkward, painful kink in her stomach which always came when she saw the back view of a tall, lean man with black hair. One day, she was convinced, she would see that view of him, and then he'd turn round, and at that moment the ground would open under her feet and she'd be plunged into chaos.

Anna fought the kink until it unknotted itself—it had all been so long ago, five years to be precise—and in five years she had changed. The man would probably have changed as well, so nobody would ever recognise anybody, and for the millionth time she told herself that she was worrying about nothing. But the thought of that nothing always brought a flush of shame to her face.

Hastily, she went through to the kitchen, examined herself in the mirror by the sink, whipped off the flowered pinny which she had donned to finish the dusting and smoothed back an errant tress of hair which had come loose from the coil. A second glance in the mirror told her she'd done all that was necessary—Isa didn't like competition, especially with her new men friends, and this was a brand new one whom Anna had never seen before.

Isa made her entrance into the kitchen in her usual tempestuous fashion, running through the hall with her arms flung wide in greeting, but Anna was used to this now—it no longer irritated her. Isa was an up-and-coming actress and she had learned early the value of a dramatic entrance—one which would draw all eyes to herself—and after years of training, it was quite impossible for her to enter a house or a room without making a big thing of it—drawing all eyes to herself. Her shoulder-length golden hair bounced, her wide blue eyes sparkled with enthusiastic joy and her voice was pitched to reach the back rows of a smallish theatre.

'Darling Anna!' Isa waved a graceful hand at the man following her. 'This is a friend, Marcus Trent. You don't know him, of course, but you must welcome him for my sake, and I know you're going to be the greatest of friends. He's written dozens of plays and books and he's quite a well-known producer as well. Darling,' she swung round on the man, 'meet my lovely sister, Anna. She's really Annabel, as I'm Isabel, but we decided to drop the "bel" thing ages ago when we were very young. You *must* love her for my sake, promise!'

'For you, Isa—anything!' Marcus Trent had a gravelly voice which Anna didn't much care for. It was harsh and uncompromising, and just now, as he spoke to her sister, Anna was almost sure she detected a biting sarcasm in his easy reply. She glanced at him as she murmured. 'How do you do' to find his dark eyes fixed on her holding what she decided was a jeering look.

Not an attractive man—that was her first impression, although she was willing to admit that to some women he might be the bee's knees. For herself, she didn't go for the tall, dark and handsome, especially when they looked a bit surly and too self-satisfied for their own good—as though they knew what was going on in a woman's mind. Surreptitiously, she crossed her fingers, hoping that Isa wasn't thinking of this one in any permanent capacity, because if she was, she needed her head looking at. This man was far too cynical and worldly-wise for Isa, who needed somebody to worship her and boost her flagging spirits when she was in the dumps.

'Tea's nearly ready,' she murmured in the background, supporting type voice which Isa preferred the other actors in her little comedies to use. 'I'll just see to a few things while you both wash off the travel.'

As she retreated to the sink and Isa led her captive off along the passage, Anna could hear Isa's gay voice. 'Now, darling, I'll show you where everything is. Don't you think this is the most deliciously unspoiled place you've ever seen?'

So that was it! Anna's face registered amusement, a wry kind of humour. Isa was at it again, trying to sell this house, as indeed she had every right to—it was half hers to sell and she probably needed the money. As for herself, Anna would be only too glad to get it off their hands. It was miles from the main road from Swanage to Wareham where she worked in a solicitor's office and it was also a very expensive house to maintain. It was old, the main part of the fabric was Georgian and forever in need of repair.

Anna had seen an attractive small estate of new bungalows being built just outside Corfe Castle; she passed them every day on her way to and from work and she yearned for one. Small, compact, modern, convenient and every one centrally heated; one of them would be nice to live in and easy to keep clean. There would be no need for a daily woman even for the rough work and her travelling and her petrol bills would be cut in half. With that and what she would save by doing her own housework, she'd be quids in.

But Isa had brought prospective buyers here before; usually theatrical friends who appeared to think that friendship entitled them to purchase at about a quarter of what the property was worth, Isa had objected when Anna had sniffed disdainfully at three of these offers. 'I don't like to think I'm making a profit from my friends,' she had protested, 'but I simply must have some capital soon. It's all right for you, darling, plugging along in this backwater. It doesn't matter all that much what you wear or how long you wear it as long as it's still neat and tidy, but I *have* to keep up appearances. I *have* to dress well, I can't wear the same thing too often, and besides, there's Peggy. She costs me the earth!'

Isa had said the same thing each time and doubtless she'd say the same thing again today.

'What time do you want dinner?' Anna asked as her sister came into the kitchen after showing Marcus Trent where he could wash his hands. 'Or do you intend to eat somewhere on the way back to town?'

Isa smiled, a smug 'cat in the cream dish' smile. 'We're not going back tonight, darling. I thought we could stay here until tomorrow evening, if it's all right with you. It's so rarely I get a chance of talking to Marcus—really talking, I mean. You don't know how it is in town—there are just dozens of people who want to talk to him, and even if I do manage to have a word with him, he gets whipped away from me so quickly. He's very much in demand, you know. Here, I shall have him all to myself, even if it's only for a few hours, and there's so much I want to talk to him about. Don't worry, he'll settle into any odd little corner you can find for him, he'll be no trouble at all.'

Anna's heart sank. It seemed that Isa was just as trustingly naïve as ever if she could believe that! For herself, one glance at Marcus Trent's uncompromising face and she'd known instinctively that the whole man spelled trouble—but it was never any use arguing with Isa about a thing like that. Isa was five years older than herself, she had been married, had a child and had travelled around the country with repertory companies—added to this, she had been living in London for the last three years, and she was inclined to add the weight of all this experience when she leaned on Anna, making her sister subside like a pricked balloon.

Instead, Anna buried her head in the fridge, ostensibly searching for eggs, and her voice came muffled from the depths.

'He doesn't give the appearance of being the easiest person on earth to get on with—at least, that's how he strikes me, but I daresay you know best.' She withdrew her head and made a great thing about examining the

dates on the egg boxes. 'But I thought . . . . You and he
. . . You know what I mean . . .'

'Darling Anna!' Isa's laugh was a little forced, but
even that didn't spoil it. The laugh had a tinkly bell
sound, but a bell of quality—pure silver, there was
nothing brassy about it—only a hint of desperation, so
that Anna looked more closely at her sister.

'I've never gone in for anything like that, not so far,'
Isa drew little invisible patterns on the table top with the
handle of a spoon, then shrugged and made a face, 'but if
that's the way he wants it, then that's the way it'll have to
be. You know me, Anna—I've never tried to use the
casting couch as a ladder to success, but the truth is, I'm
just about at the end of my tether. I've been in the
business ever since I was twenty-one, and in nearly seven
years I've achieved a moderate success. What I mean is,
I can always get a part, but I've never starred in anything. And I'm not getting any younger. I'm at the stage
where I keep thinking it's now or never.' She examined a
minute speck on one of her fingernails and when she
raised her head, her face was a bit drawn and set in lines
of stubborn determination.

'Peggy's growing every day,' she continued. 'She
needs so much, and to give her what she needs, I need
this part, it's tailor-made for me and I know I can do it
better than anybody else, but I also know how these things
work. It's an eight-episode TV serial—it'll cost a lot of
money to produce and the company will try to cover their
bets by having a big name starring to draw the audiences.
I've come to look on this as my last real chance to break
into the top of the business. As I said, I'm nearly twenty-
eight. I can't afford to wait much longer, so this time—if
it means being nice to Marcus, I'll do it!'

'Mmm.' Anna set the eggs to hardboil and began on a few other preparations for the evening meal. For herself, she wouldn't have bothered, but if Isa and her friend were staying, she would put on a show.

Isa was worried by Anna's silence. 'Please,' she muttered, 'don't go all reproving on me!'

Anna turned to her with an understanding smile. 'Don't be silly, love. I don't blame you one little bit. If you say you need, that's good enough for me, so off you go and make a few running repairs. You don't want the image to slip when it's so important to you. Come down when you're ready and you can make the tea, everything else is on the table.'

Alone once more, Anna fetched the cooked chicken from the fridge and reached into the cutlery drawer for her sharp little boning knife. It was a soft little whistle which made her turn round swiftly—not so much the whistle as the tune being whistled. That was a part of her nightmare—it drove the colour from her cheeks and sent an icy shiver down her spine. She would remember that tune until her dying day, its evocative sultriness was branded deep into her memory and what it evoked in her conscious mind was both unpleasant and embarrassing. She shied away from the memory, but the soft melodic whistling went on, forcing her, for the first time in years, to look at the truth.

Automatically, she put words to the tune—'As soon as you walked in the joint'! It had been her party piece; she had a good voice and a gift of mimicry and she'd played Shirley Bassey's 'Big Spender' over and over until she was word-perfect and could reproduce every intonation of the original—to belt it out à la the great Shirley—but it had been a party piece she'd belted out once too often at one party too many. She raised her eyes, not seeing the kitchen; she was back in her nightmare with the lights low except for the spot which shone on her—just hearing the whistled tune and hearing Marcus Trent's gravelly voice like the knell of doom.

'Hello, Anna, it's nice to be properly introduced after all this time. Five years, isn't it?'

Through the drumming in her ears, she silently cursed the juvenile romanticism which had afflicted her when she had been eighteen, nearly nineteen. When Philip had broken her heart—as she'd thought when he broke their engagement. If only she'd been a bit older, if only she hadn't led such a sheltered life, if only she'd known a bit more—She would have been able to cope like an adult instead of behaving in such an infantile manner— and all the memories which she had crowded down into her subconscious came storming back.

She'd accepted Philip's calm, reasoned argument, that he had made a mistake, that he knew now that what he had felt for her wasn't real love but something based on a calmer, cooler emotion—and she had behaved beautifully. She hadn't made a scene and she hadn't even wept—at least, not when he was looking. It wasn't until after the wedding and the reception that she had finally lost her head. She had kissed Isa goodbye, shaken Philip's hand and wished the happy couple joy, then joined a party of other young people to go on to a nearby roadhouse-cum-motel where there was a lot of noise and a lot more champagne which, added to what she had already drunk at the wedding and reception, had made her reckless and uncaring.

She had worn her most sophisticated gown, a hand-down from Isa—she remembered it with a shudder. It had been years too old for her, black and slinky with the minimum of top and the tight skirt split on one side from ankle to thigh, and to go with it she'd been very generous with make-up, so that when she looked at her reflection in the mirror in the ladies' room, she had hardly recognised herself—and as the party had become steadily wilder and noisier, somebody had suggested she sing. Whoever it was had tipped the orchestra to play her favourite pieces and she'd wowed them with a reasonably accurate rendering of Eartha Kitt's 'Old-Fashioned Millionaire' and as an encore, 'Big Spender'.

That had been when she saw the big, dark stranger looking at her and—what the hell! She'd tossed the hand-held microphone to the band leader because she didn't really need it, not for this song, and come down off the rostrum and into the centre of the floor among all the tables to give it all she'd got—singing it for him! And when she'd finished, she had laughed wildly, seized his drink which he had hardly touched, lifted it in a mock toast and downed it in one go. It was only as the raw spirit burned its way down her throat that she realised she'd drunk a double whisky on top of all the champagne.

Try as she would, she could never remember what happened next—only noise, rather wild laughter, a mad jumble of sound and the equally mad lighting which had set her senses spinning as she had danced with him until her head whirled. How she had ended up in his motel room, she had never known, and she couldn't recall anything of what happened afterwards, not until she woke in the morning with a splitting headache and a dark head beside hers on the pillows.

She remembered his, 'Thanks, darling—a novel experience for me and one I wouldn't have missed for the world,' and then there had been the dreadful waiting time when she had squirmed herself into a curled-up hump and tried to pretend nothing had happened. It had seemed like an age but in reality had only been a few seconds while he slid out of the bed, wrapped his nudeness in a short silk robe and gone off to the bathroom.

That had been the worst moment, actually seeing a completely naked man for the first time in her life. Anna had tried to close her eyes, but they insisted on remaining open while the blood drummed in her ears and perspiration oozed from every pore and she was left with the impression of wide, powerful shoulders, a long back and one hell of a lot of uncovered skin topped by the back of a smooth, dark head. The silk robe had fluttered about his knees, and she had gulped and buried her face in the pillow until she heard the sound of the shower.

It was then she came back to life, scrambled herself into her clothes and left, the slight noise she made covered by the hissing of the shower. She had found her Mini still in the car park and had driven straight home, where she had stripped, immersed herself in a bath of very hot water as if, in some way, she could wash away her shame, and then, dressed in a sober skirt and sweater, she had burned everything connected with that night—stuffing it all into the solid fuel stove and pulling out the dampers with shaking hands; Anna also piled her cherished Shirley Bassey record into the flames.

Nobody knew, she comforted herself. The other young people would simply assume she'd left, they wouldn't question her disappearance—but she didn't find much comfort in the thought. *She* knew, and that was what mattered! But over these past five years, Anna had pushed it all to the back of her mind so that it had become a hazy dream as the sharp edges of memory were smoothed away by time. Sometimes she had been tempted to tell Isa—only what had happened, not the reason for it—but common sense had told her to do no such thing.

A secret was a secret, especially one like this, and Isa might, in some twisted way, have felt responsible. Then, later on, when Isa had troubles of her own, when she was struggling to keep Peggy on what she earned—when she'd decided she'd made a mistake in marrying Philip—then it had been too late. Anna's telling wouldn't have helped in any way, it might even have added a few quite unnecessary complications.

With a jerk, Anna came out of the past and back to the present—to the kitchen, neat and familiar, the cold chicken on the board, and she looked around dazedly. She was imagining all this, it wasn't happening to her. Fate couldn't be so cruel, not to let her go on in peace for five years and then mess everything up like this!

'W-what did you say?' and try as she would, she couldn't make her voice anything but a dry, husky mutter.

'I said,' Marcus Trent lounged against the door jamb, 'I said it's nice to be introduced properly after five years—although introductions aren't all that important, are they? We managed very well without one the last time we met.'

'Oh, God!' The knife slipped from her nerveless fingers to clatter to the floor at her feet and she raised trembling hands to cover her quivering mouth. Her eyes became saucerlike in a face from which every vestige of colour had drained away. '*You!*'

# CHAPTER TWO

'Yes, me.' Marcus sounded agreeable. 'Didn't you recognise me?'

'N-no,' she shook her head. 'How could I? I couldn't remember your face, not properly—I don't think I ever saw it, not to take it in—just your back and the back of your head.' Her trembling stopped and she became icily calm. 'I didn't think whoever it was would recognise me, I didn't think you'd remember . . .'

'You hoped you wouldn't be remembered,' he corrected. 'But did you really expect me to forget such a memorable one-night stand—so mysterious! Oh no, I'd not forget that.' He left the door to advance on her and she cowered back against the sink unit as he stooped to pick up the knife. He straightened up and ran his finger down the razor-sharp edge and looked at the wicked point. 'Definitely not! It wouldn't be wise to give you this,' he raised his eyes to her face. 'You look too shaken, you might do yourself an injury.'

'Are you going to tell Isa?' It took a great deal of courage to look him straight in the eyes and to keep her voice steady.

'Does she need telling?' He raised a black eyebrow wickedly. 'I'd have thought you'd spend cosy evenings together exchanging reminiscences. Don't forget, I know Isa fairly well, she's not mealy-mouthed and I think she's quite willing to hop into bed with me if it will get her the lead in this new production of mine. What's your motivation, Anna?'

Anna lifted her chin defiantly. All her shock and weakness was conquered and replaced by a chill determination to give as good as she got. 'My motivation?' She allowed her eyelids to droop over her grey-green eyes in a bored, world-weary fashion. 'It relieves the tedium of day-to-day life, of course,' she drawled. 'In a little place like this, life can be unutterably boring.'

She decided she didn't like him. He had summed up Isa as though she was an empty-headed, untalented, immoral little idiot, and she hated him for it. He knew nothing of the real Isa, the girl who was fired with ambition—who was determined to succeed, to get to the top of her chosen profession, the mother who would do anything to ensure her little daughter a good life. She, Anna, would take the first opportunity to warn Isa that this was a purely self-centred man—not a man to be used, even to further a career.

Her own charity was a little more wide and a bit more caring, she told herself. Isa lived in a world where lovers and living together were almost the done thing, a way of life, and so usual that anybody who didn't conform was regarded as some sort of freak. But for Marcus Trent she felt no charity at all, not even sufficient to treat him with ordinary politeness. And why should she? That was how she treated strangers, and Marcus Trent couldn't be called a stranger. True, their acquaintance had been brief, but it had also been very intimate—therefore she felt entitled to be as rude—when the opportunity arose—as she liked.

'What are you going to do?' She made it an abrupt question. 'If you're going to do and say nothing, why did you bother to remind me—why bring it out into the open . . . ?'

'But it's not all that open,' he pointed out. 'Isa doesn't know and I'll take a bet none of your friends here know either. Tell me, should you object very much if your sister knew of your little fall from grace?'

It would have been so easy to shrug it off and say 'No', but Anna couldn't do it. She *would* mind what Isa thought because, to her sister, Anna was somebody who represented home and stability—she was somebody to be depended on. Not that Isa would ever admit to such a weakness, but it was so. Isa came here to normality, to a way of life which was far removed from her own rather frenetic existence. To Isa, Anna wasn't just a person, she was a place and a way of life to escape to when the going became rough—a refuge, and Anna didn't want Isa to be deprived of that, so she became cautious.

'Ye-es,' she said judiciously, pursing her mouth and looking at him down the length of her short, straight nose, 'I think I would object. My reasons needn't conern you, but it's so.'

'They'll be the usual reasons,' he drawled cynically. 'You'd live in dread that Isa might let something slip, and this is a small community, you've got a reputation to maintain. Do you preach to your sister—try to reform her? A very unrewarding task, I should think, and there'd be no reward at all if she knew about your own peccadilloes.'

Regrettably, Anna lost her temper. 'You're speaking of Isa as though she's a fool, which shows you're no more clever than the rest of your kind! You think, because she's beautiful, she hasn't an ounce of brains in her head. I sometimes think she'd have been better off and gone further on the stage if she hadn't been so lovely to look at. Then perhaps one of your moronic producers would have realised she doesn't get by on looks alone—that she's a good actress and a very nice person. Go ahead, tell her, if you wish—see if I care!' She steadied herself and stopped raging. 'Isa would never say a word about it to anybody, that's one thing I'm quite sure of. But you wouldn't stop at telling Isa, would you? And that's what I wouldn't like. Other people wouldn't be either understanding or silent and in no time at all, it'd be all over the district. I go to the Vicarage for tea every third Sunday and I'd never get another invitation.' She paused reflectively. 'I suppose you could call me a whited sepulchre!'

'Oh, I do!' He smiled unkindly at her. 'A seemingly puritanical wench with a red thread in her bodice. A thing like that getting around would play hell with your social life.'

Anna gripped the edge of the table until her hands hurt. 'Then what's your angle?' she demanded. 'And don't tell me you haven't got one, because I wouldn't believe you. You're an opportunist!'

His chuckle, when it came, surprised her—he seemed to be enjoying himself, and she wished it wasn't at her expense.

'I like to make use of what I know,' he told her blandly.

'Hmm,' she sniffed. 'I think you mean you like to take advantage!'

'Certainly,' he was not one whit abashed. 'And this is one situation where there's definitely something to my advantage. If Isa's right when she tells me you're a marvellous typist, you're just the person I need.'

Anna sniffed again only this time, the sniff covered a

kind of relief. 'Don't be ridiculous, Mr Trent. You aren't the type to *need* anybody.'

'We all do at times.' He cleared a corner of the table of the hand mixer and bowl to sit himself on it. 'At this moment, I think I need somebody like you. As you said, Isa's a good little actress—sometimes she's quite inspired, she could be just right for the part . . .' He paused and eyed her aggravatingly.

'Oh!' Anna's eyebrows nearly disappeared into her hairline. 'Are you attempting to pressure me into something?'

'That's what I like,' he murmured. 'A quick, intelligent woman who doesn't need everything spelled out for her—who understands without having all the "i's" dotted and the "t's" crossed.'

'I've always been noted for it,' Anna murmured back. 'My intelligence, I mean,' and she smiled because although she was frightened almost to death, some part of her was enjoying this game. It puzzled her, but it was so and she accepted it. 'But don't tell me that my ability to type's the only reason, because I wouldn't believe you.'

'Better and better!' he admired. 'And you're so right! I have other problems, and I think you'll solve them beautifully.'

'Problems with lady-friends?' She shook her head while a small smile curved her lips. 'That won't wash, Mr Trent. You could deal with half a dozen at once and with your hands tied behind your back!'

Abruptly, his manner changed. The mocking smile left his face to be replaced by a haughty look. 'You don't know what you're talking about,' he ground out the words and his eyes glittered. 'You say I'm pressuring you—well, you don't know what pressures I have to put up with. I'm human . . .'

'You're human?' she made it sound like a miracle. 'Now, you *do* surprise me! I'd have thought you were more of a reptilian, perhaps something hatched out of a crocodile's egg. You have that same gaping smile, all teeth and menace.'

'And you've a nasty sharp little tongue,' he was still haughty. 'Are you going to co-operate or would you rather miss the Vicaress's tea-parties?'

Anna glared at him. 'You mean you'd tell?' and then, as she watched his implacable face. 'Yes,' she said wearily, 'I suppose you would. You're that sort, damn you. I bet you've built your whole success on other people's weaknesses.'

'Some of them,' he admitted, and then, menace thick on his tongue, 'You still haven't agreed—or did you think I could be diverted so easily.'

'No,' she sighed. 'Diverting you would be like trying to turn the Amazon so it ran backwards. All right,' with a grimace, 'you write the scenario and I'll play it, but I'll need a little prompting now and then. You couldn't expect me to be word-perfect straight away.' Isa's high heels came tapping down the passage and Anna looked up at him with a warning glint in her eyes. 'Isa gets the part?'

Now he had won, he relaxed, and nothing could have been more pleasant than his smile. 'With my blessing,' he murmured softly, 'but,' the smile remained but his eyes held a hard gleam, 'I'm having to trust you not to let me down.'

Anna nodded. 'So you will!' She grinned with real mirth and gave an aggravating giggle. 'Then will you please get out of my kitchen, I've a meal to prepare.'

Somewhere round about dawn, Anna finally fell asleep, to wake again at seven o'clock, feeling like a corpse which had been buried and dug up again—she looked like it as well, and she groaned at her reflection in the bathroom mirror. A cold shower helped, but not much, so, back in her bedroom, she began a frantic hunt through the pots and bottles of cosmetics which Isa had given her at one time or another. They were all very expensive preparations and since Isa's complexion was several shades lighter than her own, there ought to be something which would cover up the violet shadows beneath her eyes.

By half past seven, she was in the kitchen looking much as usual to a careless observer, and her first observer was very careless indeed. Philip called in on his way back from the gallops, looking very fresh-air and horsey, although he only superintended from the front seat of his estate car.

'Good morning, Anna.' He accepted a mug of coffee and dropped into a kitchen chair with a sigh of exhaustion. 'I've told Mother of our plans and she's delighted. She says it's what I should have done years ago. She was never very happy about me marrying Isa, you know.'

'*Our* plans?' Anna choked on wrath as she felt the beginnings of a headache. She had enough on her mind without this added complication. 'What's that thing growing out of your shoulders, a turnip? Because it's certainly not a head! I told you yesterday, *we* have no plans . . .'

Philip smiled in a conspiratorial way. 'I know, my dear, and I appreciate your modesty, but it was only words, wasn't it? I *do* understand, believe me, but there's really no need any longer for us to disguise the way we feel about each other. It isn't as if we were hurting anybody—Isa doesn't give a damn for me, not now, and I don't give a damn what she does. Peggy's the important one, she's the person I'm thinking of.'

'Oh, charming!' Anna couldn't help the bitterness in her voice, it came out caustically, but Philip, wrapped up in his own plans and ideas, didn't even notice it.

'I knew you'd agree with me,' he was steadily serious, 'once you'd had time to think it over.' He gave her a satisfied look. 'Yesterday, I rather sprang things on you when I should have given you more time to think. I'm sorry about that, Anna, truly I am, but everything's all right now—we'll just take up where we left off five years ago.'

Anna sighed with frustration. Philip was quite the most insensitive man she'd ever met. He couldn't see! He didn't want to see! He'd never see! He was too wrapped up in his own affairs to even notice there was a world full of people going on around him. If she yelled at him till she was black in the face, he'd still not understand. However, it was up to her to be generous, and she gave him one more chance, but she didn't pull any punches.

'I don't wish to take up where we left off five years ago, Philip, and I've no intention of starting afresh with you.' She cut bread for toast with a ferocity which suggested she wished she had his neck on the breadboard instead of an inoffensive loaf. 'There's one thing I want you to understand,' she continued quietly, although intense irritation was making her hiss the words between clenched teeth. 'I've gone off you, I thought I'd made that obvious,' and then, at his stupidly understanding smile which forgave her for telling un-truths, 'As a matter of fact, there's somebody else—has been for several years . . .'

'She means me!' Marcus Trent stood in the kitchen doorway surveying them with his sardonic smile. It slid over Anna and settled on Philip's flushed face. 'You've missed the boat, my friend—a classic case of "too little, too late". Now, run away like a good fellow, Anna and I have some business to discuss.'

Philip looked from Marcus Trent to Anna and then back again—for a second he looked undecided, and then his face cleared.

'Oh, a friend of Isa's, I suppose,' he gave his hearty open-air laugh. 'Tell him to stop playing games, Anna— I know you better than that. You wouldn't be taken in by this—this . . .' the look he gave Marcus was derisory, as though slim black trousers, white silk shirt and thin black cardigan were somehow unmanly—'this effete fellow,' he finished off with a derogatory wave of his hand. 'This is something you've thought up, Anna, because you're afraid of hurting Isa's feelings, but I've told you, there's no need for us to hide anything now. What we had was the real thing, and although I went off the rails a bit, I'm back on them now. I know what a mistake I made, I've already admitted it.'

'He sounds like the very worst type of romantic fiction, doesn't he?' Marcus lounged over to the table and poured himself a mug of coffee.

'Mmm, he does,' Anna agreed, playing up for all she was worth and only too thankful for the help. 'Very Ethel M. Dell-ish.'

'You're wrong there, darling,' Marcus reproved her. 'Nowadays, she reads a bit old-fashioned, but she was a very good writer, one with a vivid imagination. What did you think of *The Knave of Diamonds*?'

'Nap always reminds me of you,' she was sugary-sweet.

Philip drained his mug and rose to his feet, his fair complexion very flushed. 'I don't believe a word of it,' he announced in his 'no nonsense' voice, 'and anyway, Mother's coming to see you this afternoon and you can be quite honest with her—she knows how I feel about you, there are no secrets between us.'

'Goodbye, Philip.' Anna made it definite, but Philip was deep into his obstinate act.

'It's *not* goodbye, Anna.' He strode to the back door, his quite unnecessary spurs jingling. 'We'll discuss this again when we're private. I'll call tomorrow,' and with an air of determination surrounding him like a cloud, he slammed the door behind him.

'And that's that!' Marcus sat down at the table, re-filled his coffee mug and looked as though he hadn't a care in the world.

Anna sniffed, then abandoned her efforts with the bread and sat down opposite him. 'If you think that, you're as big a fool as he is,' she told him unsympathetically. 'What's more, you're a very bad judge of character. Philip's the "fight to the death" type, especially when he's in the wrong. He's noted for it!'

'Philip?' Marcus raised a dark eyebrow at her. 'Now where have I heard . . . ? Oh yes, Isa's husband. Good lord, how did she ever pick a man like him? And, if my memory serves me right, when we went into a clinch that night at the motel, you called me Philip. Was that what it was all about, had he broken your little heart?'

He sounded so unsympathetic that Anna ground her

teeth. 'He ruined my faith in men,' she contradicted firmly. 'Hearts didn't come into it.'

Marcus shrugged and looked at her speculatively. 'It's happened before and to better women than you. You'll get over it! A little of him goes a long way, doesn't it, but what I can't understand is how he ever talked Isa into marrying him.'

'I think love came into it somewhere,' Anna said tartly. 'Something you wouldn't know about, of course.'

'Of course,' he agreed amiably. 'I believe I suffered from it once, but that was a long time ago, before I knew as much about the female sex as I do today.' He flashed her a mocking grin. 'To save you a lot of trouble, you'd better pack a bag and come back to London with Isa and me.'

'Thanks for the suggestion.' Anna rose swiftly and became immensely busy with her sister's breakfast tray, 'but you'll have to excuse me this time.' She couldn't match his mockery, so she became waspish. 'I think the sheer excitement would be too much for me, and apart from that, I work—nine till four every day except for weekends, and I don't think that escaping from Philip would constitute a valid excuse for instant flight.'

Marcus leaned back in his chair and watched while she retrieved a dish of chilled grapefruit from the fridge and placed it on Isa's tray. 'We made a bargain,' he reminded her. 'You're going to come and work for me some time or another, so why not immediately?'

'I've got a job,' she hedged, 'and I think you ought to trust me for a couple of weeks while I work out my notice.'

'But I don't trust you.' She had her back to him, but she could feel his eyes boring into her. 'You skipped out on me once before, so your track record's not too good as far as I'm concerned, and in any case, this job of yours—it's only a bread and butter thing and,' she turned round to find his eyes sliding over her in a derisory fashion, 'from the looks of you, the butter's not spread all that thick.'

'No,' she flushed under his scrutiny, but she was frank. 'This house eats money. Just now, I'm saving to have the gable end re-slated and in October it'll all have to be painted outside.'

'Sell it,' he advised. 'You should have done that years ago.'

'We're trying to,' she answered him sweetly, 'but we need a good price for it.'

'So that Isa can have her share without leaving you skint?'

'I could think of another way to put it,' she answered shortly, and turned her attention back to Isa's tray, filling the milk jug and pouring boiling water into the small teapot. After which, she ignored him completely and bore the tray off upstairs.

The nerve of the man! she fumed. One night in the house and he was trying to take over—first blackmail and then an impertinent interference in her personal affairs! She hated him! She could have wept for her adolescent stupidity which had got her into this mess—if it wasn't for Isa, she would have thrown the tray and its contents all over him! But she couldn't. There *was* Isa and the role her sister wanted so desperately—and Isa would have a much better chance of keeping Peggy if she had this part and the hefty income which went with it.

As for Marcus Trent, he was no better than Philip except that he had a little more brain and far fewer manners. Anna supposed she would have to put up with him for the time being, and she also supposed that the trick of it was not to let him get under her skin. After all, she only had to wait until Isa definitely had the role she'd set her heart on and then she could cock a snook at Marcus Trent and all his works.

Isa emerged from the bathroom as Anna was going along the passage, and a spasm of near envy swept through her. It wasn't fair that Isa should be able to emerge, first thing in the morning, looking dewy fresh and utterly beautiful without a speck of make-up and her hair unbrushed. Isa's body glimmered through the diaphanous nightie and matching negligee, and that body kept the promise which her face made—it was also beautiful, slender but rounded.

'Good morning, darling,' Isa smiled, showing perfect teeth, her red lips curved enticingly and her blue eyes sparkling. 'I slept like a top. Why is it I'm always so much more comfortable here?'

'No pressures,' Anna diagnosed. 'You don't have to make an effort, so you can relax.'

'And talking of effort,' Isa took her sister's arm, thereby endangering the balance of the tray, 'anything less effortless than your captivation of Marcus last night at dinner, I've yet to see. He watched you all the time, like a stoat with a rabbit.'

'Ugh! I don't care for your simile.' Anna pretended innocence. 'And I certainly didn't notice anything,' which was a lie—she had been all too aware of his clinically probing gaze and it had taken a lot of will power to appear natural and not go into hysterics.

'Mmm.' Isa sat down at the small table in the window embrasure and looked appreciatively at her tray. 'You spoil me—I don't get this in London! There it's all go, although things are a little better now I've imported an au pair for Peggy. Should I be jealous of you, do you think?'

'Not a bit,' Anna grinned. 'I expect he was examining me as future material for a play or a book. You know the thing—the rural spinster—a dying breed, so I've been told.'

'Stop talking like that,' Isa protested. 'It'll grow on you and the next thing you know, you'll be wearing ribbed stockings and a felt hat to go with your tweed suit and lace-up shoes. Ugh!' she shuddered delicately. 'All the same, if Marcus *did* make a pass at you, I shouldn't be jealous, I should applaud his good taste. I want him for one thing only, the leading role in this TV series. As a man, he doesn't appeal—much too demanding for me—worse in fact than Philip, and he was bad enough, heaven knows. Do you know, he expected me to give up the theatre and stay home knitting things?' She cocked a well groomed eyebrow at Anna. 'How is he, by the way?'

'Horsey!' Anna sat down on the edge of the bed and watched as her sister tackled the grapefruit. 'I—er—I don't know if I should tell you this . . .'

'Then don't bother.' Isa laid down her spoon and turned her head away from the window. 'I'll tell *you*! He's been around here, pouring out his troubles in your ear—like telling you I've filed for divorce and letting you in on his plans for taking my child away from me.'

'Something like that,' Anna agreed cautiously.

'I won't let him,' Isa told her determinedly. 'Peggy stays with me and that's final! I may not be the best mother in the world, but I'm a damn sight better than *his* mother at bringing up a child—Look at the mess she made of Philip!'

'There's a little more to it than that,' Anna frowned. 'You didn't know anything about it at the time, but Philip and I . . .'

'. . . Not at the time, I didn't.' Isa screwed her lovely face into a scowl. 'That's me being honest. Do you think I'd have pinched your beau if I'd known he was yours? Not that I don't think I did you a favour, but that's with hindsight. He told me all about it when we started rowing because I wouldn't give up my career—you know the sort of thing. How he'd been swept off his feet by a pretty face which concealed only selfishness and how he'd have been much happier with you. Oh!' Isa stopped speaking and a look of comical dismay crossed her face. 'Don't tell me he's come after you again—that you're the one whom he's chosen to share his hearth and home and bring up *my* daughter!'

'That's his current idea,' Anna admitted. 'I refused, of course.'

'And a fat lot of good that will do!' Isa snapped angrily. 'The man's pig obstinate; I know, I've lived with him. He gets an idea and he sticks to it because he thought of it, which makes it right, or,' she paused and her eyes hardened, 'perhaps his mother thought of it for him, that would make it so much righter, if you see what I mean. Pack your things, darling; you're coming back to town with me. That way, I'll know you'll be safe.'

'Can't,' Anna shook her head. 'I've got a job and until I sell this house for us, I can't afford not to work—and I'm not sponging on you, you've enough expense as it is.'

Isa shrugged, apparently giving way. 'Have it your

own way, Anna, but I warn you—if I see you getting in above your depth, I'll *do* something about it! I'm not having you at the beck and call of that insensitive clot for the rest of your life. Oh, my God,' as a thought struck her, 'you're not still crazy about him, are you?'

'Not one little bit,' Anna assured her cheerfully, 'but I did think you loved him once,' and then she gaped as Isa turned a brightly smiling face.

'And I thought I did,' she admitted ruefully, 'but what else could you expect? I'd just finished a gruelling six months in the provinces, understudying Juliet. All that syrupy love, all the drama, the tragedy, and I only had a bit part. It was enough to drive what little sense I had out of my mind—especially when I knew I'd have made a much better Juliet, given the chance. I wasn't in love at all, I was merely frustrated!'

Anna went back downstairs in a quandary. Why couldn't she, while she had the chance, have been equally frank with Isa? She was almost sure her sister would have understood. Mentally, she rehearsed it— what she would have had to say.

'Look, Isa, I was very young at the time and Philip's chucking me over nearly broke my heart. I think I went a little bit mad,' and then, 'I went to a party the evening of your wedding day, had far too much to drink, I wasn't used to it, you know that, and I ended up in Marcus Trent's bed.' Then she would give a gay laugh. 'Quite a coincidence, don't you think?'

But she knew she'd never be able to say the words, not because of her sister's reaction but because of her own. Each time she thought about it, she became a welter of sickened shame. Maybe she was old-fashioned, getting hot and bothered about something which many a modern miss would take in her stride, but that was the way she was made and she had to live with it. All the same, it was most unkind of Fate to arrange things so that she was now remembering things which had been buried in her subconscious for so long.

'But, my dear Anna,' Mrs Carew—small, very fair, very delicate-looking and as tough as old boots—beamed at her as they sat together in the garden. The May sun was quite warm and Anna had provided a pitcher of home-made lemonade since it was too early for tea. The older lady smiled understandingly and continued, flattening out opposition with a juggernaut ability, 'It's been no trouble at all, coming to see you. Philip drove me to your gate and then went back to the house to make a couple of phone calls. He wanted us to have a private talk—he's coming back for me about five, so that gives us over an hour and a half.'

'But we've nothing really to talk about,' Anna objected.

'We have, my dear.' Philip's mother gave her an understanding smile. 'My boy's told me of your objections, how you think he's being premature, and I quite agree with you. I understand the way you feel, I'm sure that I should feel the same in your position, but on the other hand, I can't help thinking Philip's right to strike while the iron's hot—get all the messy little details cleared up well beforehand. It will give you both a fresh, clean start, don't you agree?'

Anna didn't and said so. 'No, I definitely don't agree. It's not only that Philip's offer's premature, which I thought in very bad taste since he's still married to my sister—but that's by the way. I've other reasons for refusing him, and the main one is that I just don't want to marry him.'

'And of course I understand that as well.' Mrs Carew became even more understanding so that Anna was forced to the conclusion that she'd been reading a book on psychology, so glibly did the phrases roll from her lips. 'You've conditioned yourself, my dear, to think of Philip as Isa's husband—you've established a mental block against him, but you truly don't have to feel guilty about loving him, not any more. Within a very short time he'll be free—you'll be able to get married and live happily ever after. You must forget that first, unfortunate marriage—Isa was never a real wife to him . . .'

'She *must* have been,' Anna interrupted doggedly, 'Peggy's the proof of that, but won't you please listen when I say that I haven't been conditioned, that I don't have a mental block, nor do I feel guilty. I've just gone off him!'

Philip's mother sighed sympathetically, but she didn't give an inch. 'That's only what you've made yourself think, my dear, and I've told Philip, it'll be a long time before you realise you do still love him. I know you think he treated you badly, but is that really true? Didn't he come and tell you himself?' Her voice warmed to a hearty note. 'You know he did! A lot of men in his position would have simply written you a note, but my Philip's too honourable to take the easy way out. It's the way I've brought him up, he's been a good son to me, and he'll make you a splendid husband.'

'Not me, he won't,' Anna heard herself muttering, and she wondered how many times she would have to say the same thing before it penetrated the two Carew heads. Out of the corner of her eye she saw Marcus and Isa at the back gate, and breathed a sigh of relief while she prayed like mad that either or both of them would make their way to where she was sitting. She was thoroughly exhausted by this gentle but determined bullying. Isa went up the path and straight into the house, which was understandable—she had never liked Philip's mother—but Marcus made his leisurely way across to them where they sat on the lawn.

Quietly she introduced them, 'Marcus Trent—Mrs Carew,' and then brightly because Marcus was scowling, 'Mrs Carew is Philip's mother, Marcus.'

'I noticed the resemblance.' He was suavely nasty, but Philip's mother took it all in her stride.

'Mr Trent, you've come down for the weekend with Isa, so my son tells me. I hope you're enjoying this part of the country and the beautiful weather.'

'I brought Isa down to see her sister,' he corrected, 'but I'm spending the weekend with Anna. We're old friends.'

'Oh!' For a moment, Mrs Carew looked at a loss, but she swiftly recovered. 'I thought, from what Philip, my son, told me, that you and Isa . . .'

'It's misleading,' Marcus paused with relish. 'Isa and I have only known each other a very short time, we both have interests in the theatre, but Anna and I are very old—' his smile glimmered across the table, daring Anna—asking a question, and Anna gulped. He was going to tell Philip's mother unless she stopped him—it was there in his face, and Mrs Carew was the last person she wanted told.

'We're very old acquaintances,' she broke in before he could say any more. 'In fact, Marcus has come down this weekend specially to offer me a job with him. I'm thinking it over, but I'm almost certain I shall accept. It will mean my going to London, which will be a wrench, but the pay he's offering's a great inducement,' and her smile at him dared him to deny it. Marcus didn't attempt to deny anything, he seated himself in a garden chair and just sat, staring at Mrs Carew and showing no sign of moving while he dissected her for a new play or book. This put an effective end to any of the private conversation which Philip's mother wished to have—it put an end to any conversation, and Anna could only feel relief when Philip drove up an hour early to pick up his mother.

'Don't bother with tea for us,' Philip said the usual thing. 'We're not staying long.'

At which Marcus stirred himself and said 'Good!' Isa hadn't reappeared from the house and the little group of four sat in an uncomfortable silence for a very long five minutes until Mrs Carew remembered she had to change for church and would be late for evening service if she didn't leave immediately.

Anna watched son and mother walk down to the gate, and turned on Marcus as soon as they were out of earshot. 'You're like blight on a rose bush,' she scowled at him. 'Haven't you any manners at all?'

'None,' he said cheerfully. 'Mostly, I find they're a waste of time. If a person says they're not staying long, why try and talk them into wasting your time and theirs? Let them go.'

'But they expected me to give them tea,' she protested.

'Then they should have said so!' He was aggravatingly calm. 'I've no time for people who say one thing and mean another. By the way, I'm very pleased you've accepted my proposition.'

'And what chance did I have to refuse?' she questioned bitterly. 'You couldn't have chosen anyone I'd rather not have known the truth, and I suppose you would have spilled it all out, every disgusting detail, if I hadn't agreed,' and at his emphatic nod, she picked up the jug of lemonade, poured herself another drink and contemplated what remained in the jug. About half a pint, she estimated, plus half a dozen large ice cubes which had not yet melted.

For a moment she was tempted to empty the lot over his arrogant head, but she restrained herself—his bad manners wouldn't excuse hers—so she drained her glass and went off into the house with a caustic, 'I'm going to make a pot of tea—if you want some, come and get it—if not, stay where you are!'

Isa was already in the kitchen, pouring water into the teapot. 'They've gone?' and at Anna's nod, 'Thank goodness for that. I could never cope with one Carew, never mind two.' She gave her sister a searching look. 'You can't cope either, by the look of you—want a cup of tea?'

'Make it hemlock.' Anna sank on to a hard kitchen chair. 'I wish I could be as rude as Marcus.'

'And speaking of Marcus,' Isa drifted to the table with a filled tea-cup, her silk dress floating gracefully about her legs, 'why didn't you tell me you knew him—why all the secrecy?'

'Isa,' Anna heard her voice growing desperate, 'would you believe me if I told you I didn't know I knew him?'

'You're looking very shaken, darling, and you're not

making a lot of sense. Drink your tea and pull yourself together.'

'Life's becoming too much for me,' Anna gloomed. 'I think I shall hie me to a nunnery or hibernate till next spring.'

'Poor you,' Isa put a comforting arm about her sister's shoulders. 'Not another word till you've drunk your tea—then you can tell me all about it, if you like.'

'I'd rather not,' Anna shook her head wearily. 'No hard feelings, you understand, but it's a private matter . . .'

'Suspicious!' Isa removed her arm and stood back. 'You're one hell of a girl for secrets. I shall ask Marcus as soon as he comes in. It was quite a shock when he told me you were old friends.' She paused as he wandered into the kitchen. 'Just the man I want to see! What's going on here, and why didn't Anna tell me about it?'

'Mainly, dear Isa, because it's none of your damn business.' He sat down at the table and looked at Isa's fair face until it flushed. 'Now, if you'll leave us—Anna and I have a few things to discuss.'

'And I'm not included.' Isa slid a sly look at Anna, who was still glooming. 'I think my little sister can do with some help—she's a shorn lamb and no match for you. I won't have her bullied.'

'Isa,' his voice, his whole manner, held an undefinable menace, 'you want that part in the TV series?'

Isa forgot about being beautiful, controlling her gestures and pitching her voice. It rose to a shrill squeak of excitement. 'You mean I'm in there with a chance?'

'You're a dead cert, providing you can obey stage directions, so . . .' he raised an eyebrow and looked pointedly at the door. Isa hesitated only a very little.

'It's all right.' Anna gave her a cool smile. Now that the crunch was coming, she felt immeasurably better. Marcus might use blackmail, but it would be of the cerebral type, not the emotional variety as used by the Carews, and Anna prided herself on being cerebral. He would try to ride rough-shod over her, but at least he'd be honest about what he wanted her to do. He wouldn't wrap it up in false lover's language, like some she could mention.

'It's all right,' she repeated as Isa hovered uncertainly. 'This lamb has teeth with a cutting edge. I can manage.'

'Then I'm off to study the script!' Everything else was forgotten as Isa fled through the door.

'She has it with her?' Anna quirked an eyebrow.

Marcus chuckled at her ignorance. 'She takes it to bed with her!'

# CHAPTER THREE

ANNA had read about pregnant pauses, but now, for the first time, she experienced one. The kitchen became very quiet and the whole atmosphere was full of the feeling that something unnameable was going to happen—and yet everything looked very ordinary. She and Marcus were sitting, like two civilised people, one on either side of the table, and the afternoon sun sent long, lazy rays through the window to make pools of golden light on the walls and floor.

She sat rigidly still, almost as though if she moved or spoke something would erupt. Fate had been very unkind to her! Of all the men she could have chosen to misbehave herself with, Marcus was the worst, and it was peculiar to think that it had been a few glasses of champagne which had clouded her judgment—champagne and a stupid, hysterical, childish idea that her life had been no longer worth living. With a great effort she broke the silence.

'You can clear a room quicker than Typhoid Mary,' she sounded coolly admiring but her fingers were crisped into claws. 'But if you've anything to say, I wish you'd hurry—you've very little time, you'll have to be leaving soon.'

'Time enough,' Marcus waved aside the long journey back to London as being of little consequence. 'How soon can you be ready to pack up and leave?'

'Two months,' she answered promptly—now that

battle had commenced, her wits were working once more.

'Make it two days,' he advised.

'Oh no!' She launched into a long list of things which would have to be done—the house closed, the furniture put under covers, her dog to be fetched from the vet's little hospital. 'In fact,' she concluded regretfully, 'I don't think I could manage it under three months.'

'You'll do it in two days, and you'll need your passport.' Marcus wasn't suggesting, he was ordering, and Anna felt the hairs on the back of her neck rise—but she maintained her cool under this great provocation.

'I don't think there's much to choose between you and Philip,' she observed bitingly, 'except that of the two, he has slightly the better manners. Neither of you seem to listen to a word I say! I put Philip's deafness down to a horsey way of life, continually giving orders and never getting a reply—What's your excuse?'

Marcus smiled at her approvingly. 'I don't use excuses—I have reasons, and the reason I want you in London within two days is that we're going to France on Saturday. That's also why you'll need your passport, so be a good girl and root it out.'

'Of all the nerve!' But a reluctant smile curved her mouth. 'I don't recall being asked, but if I had been, I think you would have heard my "*no*" several miles away.'

'Early this morning,' he reminded her, 'you heard me tell your Philip we were going to talk business. That was the time to object, but you didn't. You stood there and smirked. Heavens, woman, it's a simple business proposition I'm offering. You're a good shorthand-typist, aren't you?'

'You want my speeds?'

'I want somebody who can type what I write without altering a word or a comma,' he corrected. 'I want her full-time—available when I need her, even if it's three o'clock in the morning.'

'Very unsocial hours!' Anna pulled a face, felt the side of the teapot, decided it was still hot enough to drink and poured herself a cup while she felt an odd sort of courage well up inside her. 'Offhand, I can't think of anybody who'd even consider a job like that, but if I ever do, I'll let you know.'

'Deliberately misunderstanding me won't get you anywhere,' he snorted.

'But I'm *not* misunderstanding you,' she told him sweetly. 'Like Philip, you haven't been listening to me. I've told you, I have a job—one I like and which doesn't involve night work. Furthermore, I've told you, I'm quite happy here. So what makes you think I'd exchange what I have for what you're offering?'

'I thought we'd agreed to help each other?' Marcus said silkily. 'I'd help you with your problems and you'd help me with mine, for auld lang syne—or, to put it more bluntly, for the sake of a wild night five years ago.'

'Ye-es,' she admitted reluctantly, 'but I think I'd better make one thing plain. Besides going off Philip, I've gone off wild nights as well—they're bad for my complexion.'

'Which is superb, and if you dressed decently, you'd be quite striking.' Marcus leaned back, satisfied the battle had been won. 'I'll see to that when I get you to London. Now, be a good girl, trot along and get started on your packing. I'll collect my things and rout Isa from her hideaway—it's time she and I were leaving.' And with a valedictory smile, he left Anna sitting at the table and gasping for breath.

Her first impulse was to crawl as far as the dining room and pour herself a very large whisky—she felt as though she'd been run over by a tank, but drinking at five in the afternoon wasn't a procedure she could recommend—experience had taught her that! It would fuddle her brain, so she plugged in the coffee percolator and made herself a strong brew. She hoped it would help, but something inside her head was telling her she was beyond help.

Isa erupted into the kitchen only a few minutes after Marcus had left. This time there was no studied elegance, no throwing of the voice and no attempt to look more beautiful than she was.

'Darling Anna, wish me well.' Anna was surprised to see perfectly natural tears in Isa's deep blue eyes. 'The first time!' her sister marvelled, 'the very first time! Do you realise, Anna, this is my big chance—the one I've been waiting all my life for. Nothing's going to stop me now, I promise—after this, Isa Carew's going to be a household name! No more crawling on my knees for decent parts—I can hardly believe it! Fame, security—they're just waiting for me to reach out and grab them—I'm going to have them at last!'

It was all very disjointed and emotional, and the tears of joy streamed unchecked down Isa's face. 'Oh, I know,' she wiped the worst away with the back of her hand, 'I'm going to look hideous, but this once, I don't care. A decent flat, maybe even a house—a proper nanny for Peggy instead of an au pair. I'll be able to afford that wizard kindergarten for her and later on, the

school fees—I can hardly believe it, but I *will* believe it.
Thank you, my darling Anna!'

'Thank me?' Anna raised her eyebrows as she handed
her sister a length of kitchen roll to mop up her face.

'Yes—you!' Isa beamed through the tears. 'Marcus
told me to thank you and I can't even think of anything
really adequate to say. He's just told me it was between
me and a household name, but he and the director
weren't sure if I could handle it, I always seemed to be
trying too hard and it showed. But since he's seen me
down here with you, he's realised I need more self-
assurance, and somehow or another you give it to me. So
they're going to take a chance on an unknown. You give
me confidence, darling, and Marcus says you'll be there
all the time, so that when I get uptight I can fly straight to
you.'

Isa gave a watery chuckle, mopped up her face once
more and sparkled through fresh tears. 'All these years,'
she continued, 'and I've only just discovered I need your
steadying influence until I'm completely sure of myself. I
won't let you down, I promise.' The tears began to roll
once more and Anna reached for another piece of
kitchen roll.

'Have a cup of coffee,' she offered in a flatly practical
voice, 'and pull yourself together. You'll have a pink
nose!'

'Darling, *practical* Anna—I don't care if I look
hideous, I'm so happy!'

Anna felt despair grow inside her, making her eyes
cloud so that the afternoon sun grew dim and the warm
kitchen chilly. It would be so easy to put the book
straight. All she had to do was say a few words—Isa
would believe her. Say, 'Look, Isa, your Marcus is a

conniving bastard. He's pulling strings and he's got you
and me jumping to his tune. There's not a thing wrong
with your self-confidence! He's just made an arrangement with me—you get the part and I . . .' But as she
thought it, she knew she'd never say it. It would wipe all
the shining happiness from Isa's face, and from that
moment on, her sister *would* lack confidence!

And when it came to the part where she had to explain
just how Marcus could pull her, Anna's strings . . . How
could she say it when just thinking about it made her
sick? Instead, she poured a couple of cups of coffee,
pushed one across to her sister and held on to her calm
expression. 'I'm very pleased with what's happened for
you,' she said, 'you deserve every bit of good luck you're
having. Mind you make a success of it, you are *not* to be a
flop, remember!'

'Not a chance!' Isa's tears had dried and she was
radiant. 'You realise what this means? There's no need
for you to sell this house, if you don't want to. It's where
you were born, it's your home, and I'll be able to come
down often and relax. I don't think I've ever envisaged
the day when I'd be able to say "I don't need the
money", but that day will be here soon, so you can have
my share of the place—I'll give it to you.'

'You've given enough already,' Anna said curtly. 'In
any case, I don't think I could . . .' then she stopped
speaking as Marcus opened the door and came in.

'Hurry up, Isa, I can't wait all night—I've brought
down your case.'

'Put it in the car, darling.' Isa was on top of the world.

'Put it there yourself, I want a word with Anna.' It was
almost a snarl, and Anna raised her eyebrows as her
sister went obediently to collect her things.

'Another room clearance?' she enquired frostily. 'I'll say one thing for you—your self-confidence is going to overreach itself one of these days, and I hope I'm there when it happens. I'd love to see you fall down and get your face dirty! Fancy spinning that yarn to Isa—there's nothing the matter with her self-confidence, as you very well know, so how dare you try to give her the next best thing to an inferiority complex just to further some lousy little scheme of your own!'

He held out his hand to her as though he expected her to put something into it, so she took it and gave it a limp shake. 'So glad to have met you,' she murmured with just the right amount of vagueness. 'You must come again some time.'

'If you renege on our deal, Anna, so shall I.' Marcus made it pleasantly conversational. 'Have you found that passport?'

'Give me time,' she snapped back at him. 'I haven't had a chance to look for it yet. As soon as I come across it, I'll send it on to you, but I'm afraid it mightn't reach you in time for whatever you're planning.'

His brows drew together in a frown—a bad-tempered frown. 'Two days,' he reminded her.

'With luck,' she pretended to vagueness. 'I have to find the thing, you know. It's not like my driving licence, I don't keep it handy, and things like that have a way of losing themselves.'

'Oh, I hope not,' he purred. 'I'm sure you take very good care of it,' and he swept her to her feet with an arm about her waist and practically hauled her to the front door from where they could see Isa seated in the front of the Mercedes, head down in a sheaf of typescript. 'I'll send you a reminder tomorrow,' he promised.

'Mmm,' she agreed, looking vague. 'That'll be the best thing to do, I've got a shocking memory—look how I forgot you!' She listened to his grim chuckle and waved her sister goodbye before going back into the house and closing the door firmly. The coffee was still hot and after pouring herself a cup, she sat down at the table and buried her head in her hands.

All of this because of what she'd thought was a broken heart five years ago—it wasn't fair! And with a person like Marcus Trent—she couldn't think of anybody who appealed to her less, unless it was Philip. Marcus had not one saving grace—he was arrogant, totally devoid of charm and he drove a hard bargain—but there *must* be a way out—there *had* to be, because not only didn't she wish to work for him—she never wanted to see him again! Feeling desperately sorry for herself, she piled the coffee cups in the sink and inspected the fridge for something quick and easy for her evening meal.

Halfway through the Spanish omelette which she was eating with a small side salad—and over the noise of the washing machine which was thundering its way through the soiled bedlinen which she had stripped from the visitor's beds while she was tidying the rooms—Anna heard the sound of tyres on the gravel drive. With a muttered imprecation she glanced at her watch. It was nearly nine o'clock and she was in no mood for more visitors.

She cut herself another slice of omelette and decided she would ignore any knocking, but she was given no chance to ignore anything. The front door opened and then closed and there was the sound of footsteps in the hall. Angrily, she looked up from her plate when the door behind her opened.

'There's a perfectly good knocker on that front door,' she shouted sarcastically. 'Or do you think this is a railway terminus?' And then, *'Oh!'* as she turned her head to the intruder—to Philip who was standing close behind her, looking as though he had some inalienable right to walk into her house both unannounced and uninvited.

And she'd been so sure it was Marcus Trent, it was just the sort of thing he'd do—invade her privacy—but, she scolded herself for seeing bogeys where none existed, it couldn't have been Marcus, he'd have had no time to get to London and back, even in a Mercedes.

'What do *you* want?' She was surly and ungracious, she sounded it, and she didn't care. Enough was enough for one day and she was in no mood to cope with any more.

'I came to have a talk with you.' Philip pulled up a chair and sat down, beaming at her across the width of the table. 'Now your visitors have gone, I thought we might be able to get things straight.'

'What's not straight about them?' she enquired irritably. 'I thought I'd made myself painfully clear this morning—or do you have cloth ears?'

'How could we have straightened anything out, Anna?' Philip made a wry grimace. 'The place is like a madhouse when Isa comes. It's worse when she brings one of her theatrical friends, but now we're alone, we'll be able to get somewhere.'

Anna dropped her fork on her plate with a clatter and looked across at him, her lips compressed and her eyes blazing with annoyance. 'Physically, I'm not able to throw you out,' she told him, 'And since you've obviously lost every trace of good manners, I suppose I'll have to listen to what you say—but keep it as short as possible, please, I'm too tired to deal with anything mind-bending.'

Philip needed no second invitation. He hitched his chair closer to the table, rested his elbows on the melamine top and launched into an explanation. He'd had the offer of a house on Wareham Heath—one with plenty of land attached to it.

'So?' Anna yawned delicately behind her fingers.

'So I'd move the stables, don't you see?' He became quite excited. 'Not the hacks and ponies, they can stay where they are, and I'll put in a riding manager to see to the trekking part of the business—I'll just move the hunters and bloodstock. There'll be room for all of us there, it's a very big house—room for you and me, Peggy and Mother, and I'll build new stables. It will be a family venture—Mother will sell our house, you'll sell this one, and that would give us the purchase price with quite a bit left over for improvements. I've had a talk with the estate agent, he's quoted me a good price for Mother's house and he says this place ought to bring about sixty thousand—although I think we ought to be satisfied with fifty, we don't want to be too greedy, do we? And if we ask too much, we shan't get a quick sale.'

'Twenty-five,' Anna corrected him before she crammed a lettuce leaf into her mouth.

Philip smiled at her as though she was a moron. 'No, darling,' he patted her hand. 'You haven't a lot of business sense, have you? I wouldn't let you sell for twenty-five, you'd be giving it away at that price. These small Georgian places are fetching the earth nowadays, now that Dorset's dragging itself into the twentieth century—now that people have discovered it's every bit as beautiful as Devon and only half the distance from London . . .'

Anna swallowed her lettuce and her soft mouth firmed—there was also a look of distaste in her eyes as she interrupted. '. . . You've got it wrong, Philip. I'll certainly ask for fifty, as you said, but there's Isa's share to be paid. She and I are splitting, fifty-fifty.'

Philip brushed it aside. 'Silly girl!' he smiled at her fondly. 'Do you think I'd allow you to give half to Isa? In my opinion, she's had more than enough already. She'll not get another penny out of me.'

'*You* won't be giving it,' she answered tartly. 'It hasn't anything to do with *you*! It's strictly between Isa and me. Technically, the house and everything it contains is hers—she inherited it from her mother, who inherited it from my father, who didn't make a will.'

'We'll contest that.' His blue eyes glittered like chips of Polar ice. 'I'll see my solicitor first thing in the morning . . .'

'You do that,' Anna snarled badtemperedly, 'and when he asks who you're representing, you tell him it's yourself and see where that gets you. He'll throw you out on your ear, I hope!'

'But it's not fair, don't you see?' Philip tried to make her see reason. 'Listen to me, Anna . . .' but she wouldn't. Instead she gave voice to a long-harboured resentment.

'And as for you not giving Isa another penny, that's a laugh for a start! You've never given her a cent, she's always kept herself, and what's more, you've never helped her with Peggy. She's always paid for everything, so what are you beefing about—and,' she went on swiftly because it looked as though he was going to interrupt her interruption, 'don't you come here telling *me* what's right and what's wrong. Isa and I have always considered ourselves sisters, we've always shared. If I'd had everything, I'd have given her half . . .'

'Darling,' Philip was understanding, 'that's what I mean, you're lovely and you've got a generous nature. People always take advantage of you—you need somebody like me to protect you . . .'

'I need you like I need smallpox!' she spat, and then, collecting herself, she wiped away every trace of temper from her face and tried to relax, although her hands were clenched so tightly together, she didn't think she'd ever be able to prise them apart. 'Please go,' she said in a stately, cool little voice. 'I don't think I like this conversation—and while you're going home, here are my thoughts for the day,' her temper was rising again and she felt a lot of her coolness vanishing. She raised glittering eyes in a flushed face. 'I wouldn't marry you if you were hung all over with diamonds—I wouldn't live in the same house as your mother for all the tea in China—and I don't ever want to see or speak to you again!'

Philip went, reluctantly and protesting all the way, but he went, and when he'd gone, Anna locked both the outside doors and all the windows and fled upstairs to her room. Thank goodness, she'd learned a little sense as she'd grown up. Five years ago she had had a very lucky escape, and the thought of the fate she'd missed brought her out in a cold dew of perspiration. She would be eternally grateful to Isa for saving her from that!

Gradually her sense of humour returned and she found herself smiling at the thought of Philip's discomfiture. Had he really thought she was an heiress? she wondered. Fancy him going to all that trouble just to secure enough money to enlarge his stables! And then for him to find he was making up to the wrong sister after all—she giggled. Poor Philip—serve him right!

The telephone rang insistently and Anna stopped typing Mrs Stott's new will—the fourth in as many years—and reached for the receiver.

'Beresford and Blunt, solicitors.' She had a good telephone voice, quiet yet clear.

'Good morning, Anna—have you found that passport yet?'

'Oh!' she scowled at the mouthpiece as though the black plasic needed disinfecting. 'It's *you*! The answer's "no", although I didn't stay up all night looking for it as you no doubt expected. Please get off this line, it's for business purposes only, not for idle chat.'

'Liar!' Marcus's harsh voice sounded incredibly good-tempered. 'You damn well know where it is—you're being deliberately obstructive. Isa says you're the best organised person she's ever known—you never lose anything!'

'So, I know where it is,' she restrained her desire to shout. 'I just don't care to be bulldozed.'

'Who's bulldozing?' he enquired. 'I thought we had it all straightened out.'

'Not another one!' she moaned. 'The world seems to be full of people who want to straighten me out . . .' and she put her hand over the mouthpiece as old Mr Beresford came out of his inner sanctum.

'For me?' He mouthed the words at her silently and she shook her head.

'For me,' she breathed back at him, and fluttered her lashes. 'An admirer, very pressing.' She removed her hand and in a very precise voice: 'Er—I'm not too sure of the finer points, so could you give me some details, please?'

Marcus caught on very quickly. 'Somebody with you?' and she 'Ummed' as she watched her boss retire into his office, 'Then listen, I want you here in London tomorrow. We'll have a working lunch and thrash things out, how's that?'

The door closed behind Mr Beresford and Anna abandoned her cool precision. 'You may not work for a living, but I do, and my time's not my own. I can't take a day off whenever I fancy.'

'I work a damn sight harder than you do, my girl,' Marcus snapped back. 'So you just listen to me. Give in your notice, tell whoever it is that you're leaving as from today—and don't try to tell me there aren't at least six girls with their tongues hanging out to have your job, because I wouldn't believe it. Come up to town tomorrow, there's a fast train which gets in about noon. I'll meet you.'

'What a charming request!' For a moment Anna had been tempted to say, 'I can't do that' and then hang up, but Fate, in the person of Marcus Trent, was offering her a way of avoiding Philip. Last night hadn't been the end and she knew it. Philip was the persistent type, he'd be calling this evening, acting as though she hadn't practically thrown him out, and he'd come back night after night—what he called perseverance; it worked well with his horses!

The thought of verbal battles with Philip was exhausting, but fencing with Marcus—her eyes sparkled with anticipation—that could be both exciting and exhilarating. At least, it would be something new. Marcus interrupted her thought harshly.

'Did you hear what I said? For heaven's sake, stop dithering! Do as I say!'

'Which sounds to me like a takeover bid.'

'Could be,' he chuckled harshly. 'Then let's just say I'm taking over. Noon tomorrow—and don't forget, pack in that twopenny-halfpenny job and bring your passport. After lunch, we'll go and see Isa.'

'Mmm.' Anna was steady, although her pulse had quickened at the thought of doing something different from her daily routine. 'I think I'd like that.'

She knew there would be no difficulty in giving up her job—nobody, least of all Mr Beresford, would get down on their knees and with tears in their eyes beg her to remain. The Beresford of Beresford and Blunt had an unemployed granddaughter whose mother wanted her to be employed locally, an almost impossible feat in a small country town where jobs were as scarce as snow in June—so Anna could walk out at any time and not be missed. And as an alternative to Philip, she thought she preferred Marcus. He might be an unprincipled rogue, but he was an honest rogue in that he didn't wrap things up in fancy words and high-sounding phrases. He'd be using her, but then so was Philip, and of the two, she thought she preferred to be used by Marcus . . .

'Are you coming?' The irascible voice on the other end of the phone brought her back to the present and she scowled.

'I'm thinking about it,' she answered plaintively.

'Don't bother,' he was brutally frank. 'You haven't any choice. I've got you where I want you, my girl and when I say jump, you jump.'

Automatically Anna bristled—but of course he couldn't see that, and he couldn't see her face either, which was contorted into an expression of fiendish spitefulness. 'Meet that train,' she cooed as softly as any dove, 'and then you'll be able to judge which way I jump, won't you?' and she slammed the receiver down on the cradle with an almighty crash.

Anna finished typing Mrs Stott's will and tapped at Mr Beresford's door.

That evening, after a very hectic few hours, she congratulated herself. Everything had worked out well—Mr Beresford had accepted her typing and her notice with great calm and a barely disguised relief; everybody had their pressures, including elderly solicitors. She'd stopped off at the cottage where her daily woman lived and arranged for that lady to come in for the rest of the week to clean and close the house. She had countered the 'Ooohs' and little gasps of wonder with a tale of an extended break for an unspecified period and left the cottage secure in the knowledge that the news would be all round the district by breakfast time the next morning.

Her visit to the estate agent took the most time. He produced a neat draft which described the house in such glowing terms she hardly recognised it.

'It's only small,' she protested. 'The sort of place the doctor would have lived in. You've made it sound like Longleat! People will come expecting heaven knows what and go away disappointed.'

The agent corrected her ignorance. 'People will come

expecting woodworm, dry rot and decay, instead they'll find a well maintained property. They'll jump at it.'

Anna winced at the word 'jump', it had unpleasant connotations, and went off to the vet's in a hurry where she coped adequately with her biggest problem, which was Alphonse, her standard poodle. Here she made regretful arrangements for him to be boarded for a couple of weeks—regretful because Alphonse would have liked London. He'd be admired. There were millions of poodles about, they were a popular breed, but most people preferred the toy variety—and Alphonse was no toy! He was an overgrown standard, nearly as big as an Alsatian, but beneath his basic intelligence, which was high, there was a frivolous side to his nature. He adored attention—he thrived on it. A cry of admiration did him more good than a whole boxful of condition powders!

At home, Anna locked the doors and started packing. Most of her clothes went into two suitcases which she labelled carefully with Isa's London address and a few—enough to last her for a couple of days—went into a small hand case to take with her. Her passport—she studied it carefully and then, with a shrug, dropped it in her handbag. She wasn't burning every bridge, she comforted herself. If Marcus Trent proved to be an untenable proposition, she could always stay with Isa for a while until she found herself a job she liked better.

Some time, just as dawn was breaking, she woke with a definite sense of unease and lay quietly looking out of the window while she tracked it down, and slowly it made sense. Philip hadn't called last night. He could have been busy, but she didn't think so. Had she finally managed to get through to him? She didn't think that either. When revelation came, it was like a blinding flash of light, and she sat up in bed, huddling the covers about her shoulders against the chill of early morning.

Philip was single-minded, and all of his mind was now given to obtaining the new place on Wareham Heath. For that, he needed all the money this house would bring, and the only way he could get it would be—not to marry Anna but to heal the rift between himself and Isa. If Anna needed any other inducement to go to London, this was it. Being forced into something by Marcus Trent paled into insignificance when compared with the thought that Philip might—no, *would* now transfer his single-minded attention to her sister, and he wouldn't scruple to use Peggy as a lever!

# CHAPTER FOUR

THE train was on time and Anna stepped down on to the platform and gave a couple of flicks to her thin black suit—her best—to remove the traces of travel and adjusted the collar of her white silk blouse. She glanced along towards the exit gate and spotted Marcus striding towards her. There was an arrogant determination in his walk, in the way he cut through the other hurrying passengers and in the set of his black head as he kept his eyes on her, looking neither to left nor right.

'Good girl!' He took her case from her hand, raising an eyebrow at its smallness, then set it down beside them to put an arm firmly about her waist while his other hand tipped up her chin. 'You won't go very far on what's in that,' he murmured before he kissed her.

It was a long time since a truly personable man had kissed Anna and she found the sensation distinctly pleasant. His mouth was cool on hers and he neither slobbered nor tried to eat off her carefully applied lipstick. She appreciated it, and even when she saw, through half closed eyelids, the blinding light of a photographer's flash, she retained her poise, withdrawing only slowly. Inside she was a mess of quivering nerves, but she congratulated herself that it didn't show.

'Are you putting on a show for the press?' She lifted an eyebrow. 'I didn't think the Marcus Trents of this world needed to do things like that, tout for publicity.'

'All publicity's good,' he shrugged matter-of-factly,

but there was a gleam of humour in his eyes. 'Mystery,' he explained. 'It always goes down well with the media, especially when there's a hint of romance about it.' And Anna realised that, once again, he was quite serious. To him, publicity was to be courted for whatever he could get out of it—it wasn't to be shunned.

'Oh, I see.' She blinked, steadied herself and regained that fraction of her calm which his kiss had stolen. 'And what part am I playing in this off-the-cuff little drama? The Mysterious Miss X, the Lady in Black or the latest live-in girl-friend?'

'The latter—for the time being.' He picked up her case, kept his arm about her and hustled her off towards the exit. 'Come on, Anna, stop trying to delay things. I've got a car waiting and lunch will be ready at one.'

'You should compliment me on my co-operation,' she rebuked him. 'It wouldn't have made much of a picture if I'd been snapped smacking your face!'

'True,' he gave her a brief smile as he hustled her along, 'but I knew I could depend on you, my little dear—you wouldn't do anything undignified.'

'Not in public, perhaps,' she gasped as he whizzed her through the exit. 'But you just try anything like that when we haven't got an audience and see what it gets you! Oh, what a pity,' as she spotted the black Mercedes. 'I should have brought Alphonse, he'd have gone so well with your colour scheme.'

'Alphonse?' Marcus queried.

'Mmm.' She allowed him to stuff her into the passenger seat and when he'd come round the car and inserted himself behind the steering sheel, 'The love of my life, very French and such good company.' She kept her face studiously blank as she watched him work it out—

sorting and discarding ideas until he was satisfied.

'Not a man, the tone of your voice is all wrong—
there's a note of ownership, and I don't think you'd go
for a Frenchman. It's that crazy-looking dog of yours—
the one in the photograph Isa has of Peggy. He had a
blue satin bow in his topknot. You should have brought
him, it would have made a better picture for the news-
papers—taken away the practical, businesslike aura.'

Anna relapsed into silence while Marcus drove the car
across the river, turned down the Chelsea Embankment
and finally stopped in front of a small but elegant house
in Cheyne Walk. While she was silent, her mind went on
working. Yes, the little speech she'd prepared during the
train journey should be more than adequate; she went
over it again in her mind—it covered all the points quite
satisfactorily. She rehearsed silently a few telling
phrases to make it more convincing and her soft mouth
firmed with determination so that when he opened the
car door for her, saying, 'My home—I thought we'd talk
better here—there'll be more privacy than we'd get in a
public eatery,' she was calm and cool, unruffled.

'Mmm,' she said as he pushed her through the door
and into a small hall of such elegant proportions that it
managed to look quite large and spacious. 'This *is* a nice
house,' she agreed. 'We'll probably be able to come to
terms here, the atmosphere's right for it.'

'Come to terms!' Marcus snorted down his long nose
while he eyed her with derision. 'You know my terms,
sweetie. In there, if you want to titivate,' he nodded to
the cloakroom door. 'The dining room's the second on
the left down the passage. I'll give you five minutes.'

'You *do* have this thing about time limits,' she reproved him. 'First two days and now five minutes—it's a

bad habit, and one you should try to get out of,' but all she received in return was a mocking grin as he took the stairs two at a time.

He was far too sure of himself, that was Anna's analysis which she worked out while touching up her face, smoothing her hair and restoring the rest of her person to its normal tidiness. But—she hoped that what she had to say would wipe that self-satisfied grin right off his face. She wasn't sure of herself, she could no longer be sure of anything, but she had her pride and some courage of a sort. He shouldn't have it all his own way.

The lunch, to which they served themselves from a laden trolley, was very good. Anna refused a starter and concentrated on lobster with a salad, followed by a lemon soufflé which had been chilled to perfection. It was nearly worth the trouble of coming up to London to eat like this, she hadn't tasted anything so delicious in ages, but she drank only water, holding her hand over her glass when Marcus tilted the bottle of white wine towards her.

'I'm glad to see you've learned your lesson,' he cocked an impertinent eyebrow. 'But it's only wine, relatively harmless—not champagne.'

Anna, to whom the mere sound of a champagne cork popping brought back intolerable memories, conquered her nausea and looked up at him calmly. 'I'm a quick student,' she assured him. 'One lesson is all I ever need— and now,' as he rose to plug in the coffee machine, 'shall we discuss this bizarre situation? But first of all, before you say anything, I'd like to make it clear, I've been having a rethink about the past and it's not so frightening after all. In fact, although I haven't realised it until now, I've learned to live with it.' She saw he was about to interrupt and hurried on, 'I don't really have to be so ashamed, I did no more and a lot less than a great many girls have done, and it would only affect me if I was going to make my life among people who know me—but that's all changed now. I've put the house on the market at last and I'm going to stay here, in London, so you can tell the story to whoever you please.' It wasn't half as good a speech as she'd practised on the train—it didn't sound so logical and convincing, but it would have to do; the bare bones of her argument were the same.

She raised her eyes and saw his quick frown, then watched while it cleared to leave his face enigmatic except for the suspicion of a smile.

'I've never considered that one occasion as a weapon,' he drawled, and the smile grew as he watched the water bubbling through the filter. 'That's why I promised that role to Isa! I worked it out this way—you'd do more to help her than to help yourself, and in any case, five years is a long time. Most of the people who know you wouldn't believe the story anyway, and to anybody else it would be ancient history. There's just one thing I'm worried about—' He paused again and Anna could cheerfully have slapped his face, it looked so smug.

'I don't know if you've ever noticed it,' he continued smoothly, 'but Isa has a very slight turn in her left eye. I do hope it doesn't show up in the close-ups.'

Anna retained her calm with difficulty; she had the feeling she was playing some complicated game and not playing it very well. Marcus was blocking each move she made—she felt frustrated.

'Of course I've noticed it,' she said irritably. 'But it's never been remarked on before . . .'

'. . . No, of course not,' he interrupted her in mid-flight. 'Most of her work's been on a stage where it wouldn't be seen and what little she's done on TV has been in supporting roles where close-ups are few and far between. But this time she'll be the star—the camera will come zooming in on her more frequently to catch every little expression . . .'

'. . . And,' Anna wasn't going to be beaten, 'we've always thought of it as one of her most attractive features. That air of looking at something other people can't see. A quite famous filmstar had just the same problem, and I'm told it was most effective when she played Juliet.'

'If you're referring to Norma Shearer, she had a decided advantage,' he countered. 'She was married to the producer or director, I can't remember which.'

'And of course Isa isn't—married to the director, I mean . . .'

'A less close relationship would do,' Marcus poured coffee and handed her a cup, 'and I think I know how that could be arranged. Yesterday, after I got back, I gave it some thought, and I came up with a much better idea for you and me—one that covers all the angles. We'll become engaged!' He ignored her instant protest. 'Look, my pet, if you were fifty and had a face like the back of a bus, we'd get away with the live-in secretary bit, but, you looking as you do, we shan't. As you said on the station platform, you're going to be known as my live-in girl-friend, and that leaves a bad taste in my mouth—a live-in fiancée isn't much different, but it sounds better and it shows that my intentions are pure and honourable,' he added virtuously.

'And to think I thought we might be able to reach a compromise!' Anna said gently and sadly. 'A compromise which would be mutually agreeable.' She sighed with regret as she pushed her chair back. 'You keep changing all the terms, which isn't fair. I can't compromise with a raving lunatic.'

'I don't compromise, you know that,' he reminded her. 'So—bite the bullet, Annâ. We go to France on Saturday as an engaged couple.'

'For how long?' She was still seeking a way out and a faint frown of worry creased her forehead. He'd been quite right—for herself and to pay for her own misdeeds, she wouldn't have bothered. Marcus could have put it all in banner headlines in *The Times*, but to disappoint Isa—that was a different matter. Isa was depending on this chance, she was building her whole future around this opportunity and not only hers but Peggy's as well. She looked up and caught his gaze—there was a calculating light in his eyes and his mouth and chin looked stubborn. 'The engagement, I mean.'

'For as long as it lasts,' Marcus's reply was prompt. 'Cheer up, my reluctant fiancée, it won't be half as bad as you think. If we get on well together, we might decide to put it on a regular basis—do the thing properly and get married—after all, we've had a little practice, haven't we?'

Anna's face drained of colour and her hands clenched under cover of the tablecloth while only the sting of her nails biting into her palms kept her sane. 'It's very bad manners for you to remind me of that,' she choked out the words, but they bounced off his armour plating—a plating which, she decided, must have encased him at birth and which had been hardened and tempered by a lifetime of self-indulgence and utter disregard for his fellow men.

'You seem to need reminding!' Marcus picked up his own coffee cup and raised it in a mock toast. 'The more I think about the idea, the better I like it. We'll be doing each other a favour—I need a holiday and a nice little dragon to keep intruders at bay, while you need somebody to keep your cavalry twit off your back . . .'

'. . . I can cope with the cavalry tw—er—Philip!'

'Maybe, but can you cope with his mother? That lady will have you beat, I've met that type before. What are she and her son after—money?'

Anna leaned back in her chair and closed her eyes. 'Are you sure this isn't a play or a book and that you didn't write it?'

'I've got second sight,' he grinned at her sardonically. 'Do you want to know what happens next?' His eyes lit up with a cynical gleam. 'Of course, I'm basing this on the little Isa's told me about the sale of your house, but if I *was* writing the book, this is how it would go. Either you or she will receive a proposition which goes as follows: in return for Isa handing over everything from the house sale, the cavalry twit will undertake not to claim custody of his daughter—either that, or he'll attempt a reconciliation with Isa.'

'You *did* write the book!' Anna grimaced. 'I only hope Philip hasn't read it.'

'So—he's made a start already?' Marcus nodded. 'That's one more point in favour of my scheme—safely engaged to me, you're off the hook, Isa gets the part, and if the twit's proposal comes in writing, I hope one of you silly women keeps it safe for use in evidence.'

'And you're doing all this, taking so much trouble just from the goodness of your heart?' Anna sniffed. 'I don't believe it!'

'Certainly not.' She awarded him full marks for honesty if not for tact. 'I've got my own axe to grind. By the way, did you bring that passport?'

Silently she reached into her bag and handed over the small booklet. Marcus flipped it open, studied the particulars and then raised his head to glare at her. 'You're only twenty-three!' he accused.

'So?' Anna raised an eyebrow.

'That means you were only eighteen when . . .'

'Nearly nineteen,' she contradicted, 'and girls grow up and mature more quickly in the country. It's living so close to nature that does it.'

'Like hell it does!' His mouth folded into a straight line. 'I don't go about seducing children. This puts a different complexion on things. We'll get married straight away . . .'

'No, we won't!' Anna slammed down her coffee cup. 'You've left it a little late to start getting noble! Oh, this isn't happening—it's a dream, it *must* be. If I stay very still and close my eyes, it'll go away—*you*'ll go away!' and she suited the action to the words and allowed her lashes to droop.

'Don't be a fool,' he snapped at her. 'I've no intention of going away—you're getting hysterical . . .'

'*Yes!*' she sat bolt upright in the chair, her eyes wide open, 'I bloody well am! And who could blame me? You walk into my life and start taking over as though I was a puppet with no mind of my own, and I think,' she stifled a small sob, 'I think you're presuming too much on an acquaintance which only lasted one night. How do you know I don't do it all the time?'

Marcus pulled up a chair and sat down beside her, taking her hand in his and tightening his fingers when she tried to withdraw it. 'The cavalry twit,' he sounded amused. 'He wouldn't be hot on your trail if you behaved like that. His mother would forbid it. You might have got away with one night, but she'd soon know if you made it a regular practice.'

Anna could feel her self-control slipping away and she hung on grimly to the tattered remains of it—forcing her voice to a calm, smooth tone. She would have to give way a little, as little as possible, so she managed to colour her voice with a creepy kind of humour.

'This engagement you're so keen on—what sort of engagement is it going to be? You can hardly expect me to go round looking like wedding bells.'

Marcus accepted the olive branch. 'It depends on how good an actress you are,' he explained. 'For one thing, you'll have to stop swearing—everybody knows I don't like it in a woman. Can you look dazed with happiness, and how are you at the occasional loving embrace?' And as she cowered back in her chair, 'That's no good, you're behaving as though I was Dracula.' Firm hands grasped her shoulders, pulling her towards him. 'Melt, Anna,' he commanded, 'try to look as though you're enjoying it.'

And then his mouth was on hers and her memory of the cool, calculated kiss at the railway station faded into oblivion while her heart wept. Enjoyment was such a futile word, it didn't go one thousandth part of the way to describe what was happening to her—and it was only makebelieve, just for the effect it would have on an audience, but she could feel herself, every part of her, coming alive. Something hot uncoiled itself in her stomach and spread warmth through her whole body, making her skin more sensitive and drowning all her common sense until she was a mindless creature who wanted this to go on for ever.

'Good girl!' Through the whirling clouds of blackness, she heard Marcus's voice and suddenly she was cold. 'You did that beautifully!' And there was his finger under her chin. 'Quite starry-eyed,' he said approvingly. 'You're almost as good an actress as Isa.'

All the stars went out of her eyes and they glittered green with rage. 'Yes, I am, aren't I?' Raging against herself helped enormously. 'It's my upbringing—you know the thing—"Smile nicely at your godmother, Anna", or "Eat your cake like a good girl, it's been made specially for you".' Her voice developed a definite wobble and she drew a deep breath while she fought for control, looking at him meanwhile from under her lashes. He hadn't been affected at all! That kiss had done nothing for him—she had been sent into a seventh heaven, but for him, it was nothing.

He smiled down at her, a swift, charming smile, and she caught her breath before scolding herself for being weak and foolish. That smile and the rest of his performance, he'd probably been practising them ever since he was old enough—in his early teens, she jeered at herself. He was an arrogant pig and he used people, which made him a self-centred, arrogant pig . . .

'. . . A little more practice and you'll be perfect.' The words were coming from a long way away, but she concentrated on them and gradually came back to normal. 'Now, you'd better get acquainted with the house.' He was no longer holding her, he had a hand tucked under her elbow and was leading her out of the dining room. 'It won't do,' he continued smoothly, 'if we have visitors and you don't know your way about. Carl will show you where everything is.'

'Carl?' she queried.

'Head cook and bottlewasher.' He steered her firmly in the direction of a green baize door at the end of the passageway which ran from the hall to the back of the house. 'Don't upset him, whatever you do. He's the one person we can't manage without. He's been with me for years and if you run into any difficulties, he'll put you right—I told him to get a room ready for you so, if I point you in the right direction—I've got a few telephone calls to make.' He stopped at the green door. 'In there, it's the kitchen,' and he turned on his heel and vanished back through yet another door, closing it firmly behind him.

Left alone, Anna walked back to the front door, drawing deep breaths and her nose thinning with temper. For two pins, she would have picked up her case and walked out to hail the first taxi she saw to take her to Isa's flat, but—she flicked a glance round the immaculate hall—her case, which Marcus had dropped negligently on the floor by the hall table, had vanished. It was a good case and she wasn't leaving without it, so she walked back to the kitchen.

Anna stopped just inside the door—she hadn't known what to expect. Carl as a name meant nothing to her, but she had conjured up the image of a white-haired servitor, maybe a bit doddery, aged in the service of his master, kind and benevolent-looking, clad in a green baize apron and polishing the silver. Whatever she had expected, she wasn't prepared for a morose-looking middle-aged individual who was reading the sporting pages of a newspaper, not one who was completely bald and who looked like an ex-prizefighter or an all-in wrestler.

'Miss Gentry.' His voice was as expressionless as his face and although she forced the beginnings of a smile, it was cut off before it even got started. 'If you'll follow me, miss,' he folded the paper carefully—and like master, like man, he took it for granted she would!

Anna followed obediently up two flights of stairs where, on the top landing, Carl enumerated the doors. 'Bedroom, bedroom, your bedroom, toilet and bathroom.' He allowed her a quick peep at her own room, yellow with white muslin frills she thought, although she wasn't allowed sufficient time to make sure, and then she was led back down to the first floor where Carl went through the same routine. 'Bedroom, Mr Marcus's bedroom, bedroom, toilet and bathroom,' and before she could get her breath, he was leading the way back to the ground floor. 'Drawing room, dining room, Mr Marcus's room, your office, Miss Gentry.'

Anna was permitted to inspect her office and she dutifully admired the desk, the electric typewriter, the telephone and the filing cabinet. She even opened the desk drawers, but drew a blank except for the top left-hand one, which contained a small black address book. Carl indicated some cardboard cartons stacked along the wall.

'Stationery, Miss Gentry; you will wish to arrange it yourself. Tomorrow you will be provided with a table, some more chairs and some shelving for your reference books—and now, if you'll excuse me . . .' and he went out, closing the door behind him softly and leaving her alone.

Anna took a swift glance around and then followed him, but he had vanished back into the kitchen like a genie going back into its bottle, so she headed for the door through which Marcus had gone, her high heels clicking explosively on the polished tiles of the passage-way.

It was a small room, much smaller than the one allocated to her for work, and it was gloomy since the large window looked out on to a high hedge. Marcus looked up from the table where he was scribbling notes on a pile of foolscap sheets. 'Seen everything?'

'I've seen nothing,' she snapped. 'What does your general factotum specialise in—sign language? I suppose you know he's practically mute!'

'So,' he grinned, 'what do you want to do now?'

'Get out of here as soon as possible,' she answered promptly and then, because he frowned—so silly to be upset by a mere frown—'I'd like to go straight to Isa's, make arrangements for a bed for tonight . . .'

Marcus pushed aside his work with obvious reluctance and shook his head at her. 'You're staying here,' he told her emphatically. 'Apart from everything else, since Isa's imported that au pair, there isn't room in her place to swing a cat—the au pair's a buxom piece and I can't imagine you and her together in a single bed.'

'You're closely acquainted with Isa's flat?' Anna looked at him down her nose.

'Not that close—didn't Isa tell you?' Marcus's mouth quirked into a curve of ruefulness. 'She hadn't made her mind up about selling herself for a career. Had she offered . . .'

'You'd have accepted!'

'No-o, I don't think so,' his eyes gleamed with appreciation. 'I don't go for dedicated women, and Isa's dedicated. Besides, I'm sufficient of a swine to prefer to make my own arrangements—I don't like things handed to me on a plate. In any case, I've just been on the phone to a few working colleagues—we're giving a party to-night, an engagement party so you'll have to be here for it and since Isa's been invited, there's no need for you to go flying off to her flat. Did you bring anything to wear?'

'Not to a party,' she said with a sarcastic bite. 'You didn't make that clear on the phone yesterday.'

'How could I?' Marcus was the essence of reason. 'I hadn't thought of it yesterday—it all came to me last night when I was lying awake, thinking of you. I couldn't sleep for thoughts of you—I kept remembering what it was like five years ago.' Her heart gave a treacherous lurch as he looked at her pensively and went back to the matter in hand. 'Didn't you bring anything?'

'Not for a party,' she repeated in a mutter. 'I was going to take Isa out—a restaurant . . .'

'You should have brought that black thing you wore at the roadhouse five years ago.' His eyes slid over her assessingly. 'It was a bit old for you at the time, but it would look very good now.'

'Will you stop looking at me as though I was an exhibit in a cattle show!' she raged. 'I don't want to have an engagement party—I don't want to be engaged . . .'

'Anna!' Marcus slammed his hand down on the table-top and the noise made her jump. 'Just at present, what you want isn't very important. The only things which matter are the people who are coming tonight and the impression we make on them. Since they will be here, so will you, and if you haven't anything suitable to wear, I'll ring Isa and ask her to lend you a dress—you're about the same size.'

'No, we're not!' she contradicted triumphantly. 'I'm fatter and an inch taller.'

'Then I'll ask her for something loose, it'll cover a multitude of sins, and she can come early to give you time to dress before the others get here.' He stuffed his hand into his jacket pocket and came out with a small box. 'Wear this,' and he pushed a ring on her finger.

Anna looked down at her hand—she didn't care for rubies, they made her hair look faded, but this one wasn't too bad. It looked more like a signet than an engagement ring, and the stone was an old-fashioned cabochon cut so that it didn't sparkle to quarrel with her marmalade hair. Instead, it glowed sulkily to match her mood.

'Trappings for the occasion?' she sneered. 'A prop— something without which the actress can't take the stage? And why this?' she waggled her finger under his nose. 'It didn't have to be the real thing, you know— something out of a Christmas cracker would have been quite sufficient.'

'I am trying,' he told her patiently, 'to give an air of verisimilitude. In your defence, I might add. You want to keep that lily-white reputation, don't you?'

'*You*—speak to me of reputations!' By this time, her temper was well and truly lost. She wasn't wanting him any more, she was hating and wanting to hurt. 'I bet yours is as black as it can get, and no amount of good jewellery is going to convince anybody of anything. You can't hope to cover us with a coat of whitewash and a ruby ring.'

'But you don't know my reputation.' He was mild, although the hands gripping her arms were squeezing painfully. 'I'm well known for not taking everything that's offered—Lord, I'd be a physical wreck in no time!'

'Bragging again!' she squealed, her face flushing at the

implication of what he'd said and the last bit of her control slipping away from her.

'You aggravating little bitch!' Now he was laughing at her. 'You've got a bad mind, my darling. Did you imagine I was going to force my way into your room tonight—maybe seduce you? But I did that five years ago,' he pointed out reasonably, 'or would you rather not be reminded?'

Anna's flush had paled and while he was speaking, she had pulled herself together. 'There was I,' she almost moaned, 'living quietly, doing as I pleased, and . . .'

'. . . And your past caught up with you.' He was gently admonishing.

'Maybe,' she admitted, 'but it was only the once. I hadn't been living a life of sin or anything like that. *Oh*!' as she watched his face light up in the by now familiar sardonic grin. 'Don't you dare stand there and laugh at me! It's all right for you—it's all right for everybody except me. Isa gets what she wants—you've some rotten purpose that's going to get you what *you* want, although you won't admit it, but when it's all over, where shall I stand? That's what I want to know. And there are a few other things I want to know as well,' she added darkly.

'Fire away.' He was once more amiable.

'Then what do you want with my passport?' she demanded.

'Visas,' he explained briefly. 'Next question?'

'You don't need visas for France,' she objected, 'so that's a lie for a start!'

Marcus sighed extravagantly. 'We're going to France because I need a holiday—a rest from the continuous battle with the script writers. I've been at war with them for nearly three months, so I've earned a break. I also want to do a bit of research for my new book, and that might take us to North Africa—to somewhere where visas *are* required, so, to be on the safe side, I've told Carl to get them for any country that needs them. Now, can we pass on to your second question, please—I've never met such a fussy and fussing woman!'

'Then you must have been employing a load of zombies,' Anna retorted spiritedly. 'Second question coming up. How much are you going to pay me? Because you did make a mention of night work, something about wanting me to type at three in the morning—and, last but not least, as I said before—where do I go from here?'

Marcus relaxed visibly. 'Answer to the first part—double what you've been getting up to now, to compensate for any unsocial hours. As for where you go from here—that's up to you. If the worst comes to the worst and you feel you *have* to leave me, I'll fix you up with a job somewhere, but on the other hand, if you're sensible and marry me as I want, the problem doesn't arise. *Be* sensible, Anna. I fancy you—and you aren't all that unmoved. It'll solve a lot of problems—we can go to bed together without you feeling guilty . . .'

'I said you were demented!' she interrupted fiercely to conceal her inner fear. Marcus was so right—she was a long way from being umoved, but it wasn't love—not this thing she felt—just a sexual attraction which, once gratified, would wither in the light of day. It was a thing of the night, a hunger, an appetite which could bring gratification but not necessarily happiness. Unconsciously, she folded her arms protectively over her breasts and her face flamed at his sly chuckle.

'Thinking about it, darling?' Marcus was softly jeering as though her mind was an open book and he could read

every thought passing through her head. It chilled her so
that she could speak quite normally and without a trace
of embarrassment.

'Trying to remember,' she looked up coolly. 'But I
can't, so it couldn't have been anything so very earth-
shattering or the memory would have survived for five
years.' She lifted her chin and became prim. 'Maybe it
was a flop—If it was that good, I *should* have remembered, so I don't think I'll repeat the experience, thank
you.' She gestured at the small pile of foolscap on the
table. 'Is that for typing, because if it is, I may as well get
on with it and start earning this enormous salary.'

'The final script alterations.' Marcus was diverted,
or perhaps he was being kind and giving her a breathing space—she didn't much care which as long as she
could get off what was an uncomfortable subject. 'How
soon . . . ?' and he raised an eyebrow as she leafed
through the pages—there weren't so many of them.

'A couple of hours,' she told him sedately. 'And since
I'm here, I might as well get it done,' and without loss of
dignity, she backed off, turned and made her way back
to her office. 'At least, you'll have a sample of my work
and, who knows, I might eventually be able to kid myself
that this is a legitimate job.'

'It *is*! Strictly all above board, I assure you.'

'No, it isn't!' Anna reverted to her normal cool
approach and her English became exact, if uncom-
plimentary. 'It's something putrid you've dreamed up in
the dark recesses of your mind to get you off whatever
hook you're hung up on!' She opened the door and then
turned again to deliver what she hoped would be a coup
de grâce. 'And I don't believe that tommyrot about you
fancying me either. That's all a part and parcel with the

rest of your story—a mixture of half-truths and downright lies!' And she skipped swiftly through the opening and slammed the door violently.

# CHAPTER FIVE

Isa made an entrance into the yellow and white frilly bedroom at seven o'clock, looking younger and gayer than ever.

'Darling,' she cooed at Anna, who was seated at the dressing table and scowling into the mirror, 'you've been sneaky! No,' she corrected herself, 'that's wrong—you were never sneaky, only dreadfully self-contained. Mummy always said you'd been repressed. But why didn't you tell me you'd landed a nice plump fish like Marcus? I told you I wouldn't be jealous, but I know several ladies who'll want to tear your hair out by the roots—want to hear about them?'

'No!' Anna ignored the question and looked at her sister sternly. 'Did you bring me something to wear to this damn party?'

'But of course.' Isa opened her blue eyes very wide. 'You surely know I wouldn't let you down—or let you go to your own engagement party in one of those hideous Crimplene things you buy for visits to the Vicarage. Just to be on the safe side, I've brought two dresses—they're both brand new, never been worn, so nobody's seen them before. By the way, just for the record, I'm Isa Carew and you're Anna Gentry and we've never met before. Remember that, darling, because I'm not having anybody saying I've got this part through family connections. Several of the hags coming tonight are bitchy enough to suggest just that!'

'Very well,' Anna sighed. She was weary of deception, but for Isa's sake she would tolerate some more. Besides, Isa didn't know—she was on top of the world, and Anna wasn't going to let anything spoil her sister's golden happiness. Not Marcus's threats, not her own feeling of being trapped and not even Philip's money-orientated behaviour. Anna determined to stay well away from the subject of Philip—Isa had a flair for hitting the mark by accident.

'Do you have to have some sort of audition?' Anna asked. 'Supposing . . .' And for one brief moment she was mean enough to hope that Isa would fail, but she swiftly banished the thought from her mind. Marcus wasn't the type to start out on a course of action unless he was fairly sure it would be successful—he seemed to cover himself all ways—he *must* know that Isa would get the part or he would never have gone to such lengths. For some reason, this made her feel quite happy—she couldn't understand it and she was reluctant to analyse it . . . Isa interrupted her musings.

'Are you listening to me, Anna? That's the second time of asking, you've gone off into one of your dreams again. I was telling you, that film test will be a piece of cake. I've been dieting a bit and lost a couple of pounds, which is all to the good because the small screen puts half a stone on anybody—and I'm much better than the other girl—well, I call her a girl, but she's years too old for the part and I can act the pants off her any time.'

'It's nice to be so confident,' Anna shook her head. 'I wish I was—I'm not at all sure I'm doing the right thing. It's all been such a rush, I keep thinking . . .'

'I know, darling, but don't let it throw you. Everybody feels like that. But getting cold feet at the last moment doesn't help, and anyway, I don't see what you're worrying about. I know you're one of the cautious ones, but truly, you don't have to worry, Marcus has got it very badly indeed—well, I mean to say, he must have, mustn't he? I don't know if I ought to say this, but he *has* got a bit of a reputation, but he's never been anywhere near being tied up before. You've done very well for yourself, considering you're fresh up from the country— perhaps that's what's bowled our Marcus over. You know what I mean—you're beautifully self-possessed—I suppose it comes of sitting on all those rural committees, hobnobbing with the school governors.'

'I don't hobnob,' Anna protested. 'I only take the minutes of the meetings.'

'Oh yes, I know,' Isa waved an airy hand, 'but it's the appearance that counts. I know it's all on the surface, that underneath you're an innocent at large. I think Marcus feels all protective of you.'

'He's got a damn funny way of showing it,' Anna muttered to herself.

'And I'm afraid I shan't be able to help much.' Isa ignored the hardly audible growl. 'I'm going to be too busy getting into the part and there's bound to be untold numbers of pre-rehearsal meetings to discuss the script and things—not to mention the advance publicity. Come on, dear one, which of these dresses are you going to wear?'

Ann inspected the dress bags. 'The black, I think; I feel funereal.'

At last Isa got the message. 'Something wrong?' and Anna straightened her back with a snap. What good would it do to worry Isa? None at all—it might even make matters worse.

'No, of course there's nothing wrong. What could be? It's just that everything's happened so quickly and you know how slow I am to take to change. There's Alphonse, though—the vet's keeping him for a week, but do you think you could cope with him while I find my feet?'

'He sleeps on the floor, doesn't he?' Isa giggled. 'That being the case, he can come any time—Peggy adores him. My place is bulging at the seams, but while I couldn't put anybody up, I can always find room for a dog. Now, sit down—I'm going to do things to your face like what-has-never-been-done-before! By the time I've finished with you, nobody will be asking why Marcus is taking the plunge, they'll be asking what took him so long!'

Anna's mirror assured her she looked very good indeed. Isa had worked a minor miracle on her face so that her eyes glowed very green beneath the load of eyeshadow and mascara—her rather thin face looked softer and more rounded and her wide, soft mouth was seductively red. The black dress was a miracle of under-statement—low-cut, sleeveless and very slim but with some artistic draping of the skirt which made movement easy. She felt quite comfortable in it, which gave her a surface sophistication, but common sense told her this wasn't Isa's dress—anything of Isa's tended to fit Anna a little too well, as had the black one she had worn at that ghastly party. She smoothed the soft material down over her hips and turned from the mirror.

'This isn't one of yours.'

'Lord, no,' Isa grinned. 'Nothing of mine would fit you properly. You could have wriggled into one and got away with it at a pinch, but I thought, tonight, you ought to have something better than that, considering you'll be the centre of all eyes. I told Marcus when he phoned, so he asked me to get you a couple so you'd have a choice. I'm glad you chose that one, though, it shows you have a good sense of value—it cost twice as much as the other.'

'Damn him—and you as well,' Anna sweetened it with a smile. 'I'm being managed, and I don't think I care for it.'

'What *are* you complaining about?' Isa looked at her oddly. 'Or is something going on that I don't know about? As far as I can see, you should be down on your knees, thanking your lucky stars. You're going to marry the man, aren't you?'

'I should be down on my knees praying for a quick death,' Anna corrected as she gathered up her evening bag and took her sister's arm.

The curtains which covered the wide archway between the dining room and drawing room were looped back to make one big space and Isa halted by them, an expression of comical dismay on her face while her hand tugged at the skirt of Anna's gown. 'Oh lord, she's here!'

Anna, slightly in front halted. '*She?*' she hissed through stiff, unmoving lips and without turning her head.

'The rival,' came the desperate mutter behind her. 'The ineffable Natasha. Do you want the lowdown, or would you rather play it by ear?'

Nobody in the room had noticed them, the dozen or so people present were clustered in groups of two or three, seemingly intent on drinking as much as possible in a very short time, and Anna retreated a couple of steps to conceal herself and Isa behind the curtains.

'Tell me all,' she said wearily. 'Is this the other contender for the part—the one you think they may choose instead of you?'

'Oh, that!' Isa was muttering behind her hand and Anna was hard put to hear what was said against the babel of voices which all seemed to be talking at once and at top volume. 'Natasha's years too old. Actually, I'm more worried about you. Our Natasha—she claims to be Russian with French overtones—she's been after Marcus for years—she's the sort that hangs on like grim death. She and Marcus had something going together in Paris years ago and she's been going round telling everybody he wrote this book for her and with her in mind. Marcus escaped the Paris affair, got away by the skin of his teeth, from what I hear, but she never gives up—a right little man-eater, and our Marcus is a toothsome morsel. Will you look at that gown she's wearing! It doesn't leave much to the imagination, does it—poor Marcus!'

'Poor Marcus, my foot!' Anna scoffed. 'Look at him, he's enjoying every moment—the rat!'

'What are you going to do?' Isa muttered in a worried whisper. 'Oh, Anna, don't for heaven's sake run away. Go in and slay her, you've got youth on your side.'

Anna conquered her first inclination, which was to retreat swiftly and silently; remembering she had a part to play, she sniffed. 'If he pats her bottom once more,' she said in a deadly tone, 'I shall slay *him*! Trail along behind, Miss Carew, and duck when you see the knives flying!' and closely followed by Isa, she swept into the room and up to Marcus who was in a semi-clinch with a dark, exotic-looking woman.

'Darling!' she smiled at him, but her teeth were

showing and her eyes were glinting very green. 'Look who I found wandering about in the hall—your new star, quite overcome by shyness. How could you treat her like this? We've introduced ourselves.'

'My pet!' Marcus abandoned the exotic type and gathered Isa into his arms as though he hadn't seen her for years to plant a theatrical kiss on her mouth. 'Late as usual—but that's the best sort of entrance to make. We've all been waiting for you. Have a drink, darling, I've been saving this for you.' He moved aside to display a tray of glasses and a bottle of champagne nestling in an ice bucket. 'Guarding it with my life,' he amplified, 'everybody here's drinking like a fish.'

Seriously, he filled three glasses—there was already one full on the tray—and handed them round, giving Anna the already full one. 'And that's yours sweetheart, something very special which Carl laid on specially for you—you're entitled to something better than we give to the common herd. Now,' as the rest of the company gathered round, 'please, a toast to Anna, my first and last fiancée. I'll do the introductions properly later on.'

Anna looked dubiously at her glass and raised it reluctantly to her lips to take a small sip—a certain past event in her life had given her an allergy to champagne—but as the first bubbles hit the roof of her mouth and under cover of all the good wishes, she glanced up at Marcus and mouthed silently, 'This is ginger ale!'

'Mmm,' he half turned away from the company to murmur in her ear. 'You can't have champagne, not while we have company—remember what it did to you last time? When they've all gone, you shall have a whole bottle to yourself!'

'You are too kind,' she murmured back with a small

smile, then turned her back on him to become involved with Natasha.

'You have a small part in this production?' That was Natasha being interested.

'Oh no,' Anna shook her head, 'I'm not an actress.' Privately, she thought she was doing very well, putting on a damn good show—standing quietly within the circle of Marcus's arm and ignoring the kind pat he gave to *her* bottom. 'I'm very ordinary, a common or garden typist.'

'Don't believe her, Natasha.' Marcus's arm tightened into a hug, almost a cuddle. 'There's nothing common or garden about my Anna. She's unique in that she never performs publicly. I believe she did have one short experience, but the success put her off—she can't stand it. No, it wasn't acting,' as Natasha opened her mouth to pose a question. 'Anna sings very well, but she discovered she couldn't take success. Nowadays, she sings only for me.'

Isa caught on quickly to add her mite. 'Anna sings? How lovely! What sort of music—ballads, oratorio? Johnny shall play for her—he can play anything.'

Anna brought a slender, spiky heel down on Marcus's shoes. 'No, thank you,' she said sedately as she gave the heel a twist. 'I only sing in the bathroom nowadays—the acoustics, you know.'

'In the bathroom?' Natasha gave her a glassy smile. 'By yourself?'

'Of course,' Anna blinked innocently. 'Solos—you need two for a duet! Darling,' she jabbed her heel down again and admired Marcus's stoical endurance and indifference to pain, 'take me into a corner somewhere and give me another drink, please. I need my morale boosted.'

Out of the corner of her eye she watched the crowd dissolve about them and then, turning her back on the room, she hissed at him in a furious whisper,

'Isa said Natasha was the rival—you promised me Isa would have the role, that's why I'm . . .'

'. . . and I keep my promises.' The loving arm gave her a little shake. 'Stupid! Natasha's not an actress, and she's not Isa's rival, either on or off the stage.'

'Mine, perhaps?' Anna accepted a refill to her glass from a bottle hidden away among the green fronds of a pot plant and gulped at more ginger ale.

Marcus gave her a sly look. 'Isa's been gossiping, I suppose. You've heard about Paris?' and at her nod, 'That was all of ten years ago. A small apartment on the Left Bank—I was very young and immature . . .'

'You were never young and immature,' she muttered back. 'I think you were born as old as sin. Oh, can't you see—we'll never get away with this. Another five minutes and everybody will know it's a put-up job—I'm not in your class . . .'

'Don't worry so,' he growled back at her. 'They'll put it down to my jaded palate.' If that was meant to be comforting, Anna had no comfort from it! 'And,' he continued, 'we can always manufacture a bit of corroborative evidence—like this,' and his dark head swooped.

As a kiss, it was restrained, but still too much for Anna, who emerged several seconds later, breathless and trailing clouds of glory. One thing, she decided, when she was once more in a state to decide anything—this sort of contact with him would have to stop. She was too physically aware of him—he set her off balance, made her feel too feminine, and although she'd made a good job of not showing it, she was sure he knew. He was too experienced not to know—it was there in the cool confidence of his hold on her, in the gleam in his dark eyes and in the satisfied curve of his mouth.

'Confidence restored, morale boosted?' Marcus raised an eyebrow.

Anna gave him a wide, meaningless smile. 'Utterly, so you can take your arm away, I shan't fall over. I'm all set to mingle now,' she answered tartly but with the saccharine smile going full blast. As soon as she was free she stalked off, heading for an older type woman who looked motherly, but it was only a superficial motherliness. The lady was another dedicated actress and all she wanted to talk about was her own part in the coming production. After less than a minute the subject of her monologue changed, from how good her part was to how it could be improved, and Anna stood appalled as she realised she was expected to mention these improvements in detail to Marcus; even urge him into making alterations in the basic character of the role.

'And let that be a lesson to you!' he came and muttered sarcastically in her ear as the woman, having made her point, moved off in search of a ginnier gin and tonic.

'What on earth did she think I could do?' Anna gasped. 'Doesn't she know I don't . . .'

Marcus grinned humourlessly. 'As you've captured me, I expect she expected you to go on moving mountains! You, my little love, have achieved a feat as yet unsurpassed—you have me on my knees with my tongue hanging out!'

'That'll be the day,' Anna growled, and to give her shaking fingers something to do, she impaled a cherry on a cocktail stick and twirled it before she turned away, only to fall into the clutches, of Natasha, who was on her fifth dry Martini and waxing eloquent—not about the production but about its author.

'Dearest Marcus,' Natasha purred. 'He never changes—just the same as ever, the same as when we first met in Paris. Brusque, sometimes even rude, but only to cover his deepest feelings—I *know*!'

'I bet you do!' Anna muttered below her breath, caught a warning frown from Isa and stretched her face into an expression of interest. Isa's frown had said 'Play this one carefully.'

'I was his mistress, you know,' that was Natasha being innocently frank. 'If things had been different, we would have married.'

'Different?' Anna took another mouthful of ginger ale and dabbled her cherry in what remained in her glass before she bit into it thoughtfully. Natasha was going to give her the lowest parts of the lowdown on the Paris episode, and Anna carefully schooled her face to an expression of polite uninterest—the expression she used when she took the minutes of the Parish Council meeting when all sorts of embarrassing things were discussed, and if she could sit calmly through the pros and cons of siting a public lavatory next to the children's playground, she could do it now.

'Mmm, different,' Natasha nodded regretfully. 'I wasn't free. My husband was in the Diplomatic—very French, very rich but old, you understand? It was an arranged marriage and he could give me nothing except money and position—not passion—but this was what my parents had wanted for me—it was my duty . . .' Her voice tailed away as she reached for another Martini from the well filled tray at her elbow.

'How terrible!' Anna voiced a spurious sympathy. 'What a pity—I mean, didn't you ever think of leaving home, working . . . ?'

'How could I?' Natasha gave a small, sad sigh. 'What could I have done? And now it's too late. Marcus is affianced and I must live only with my memories.'

'Sad for you.' Anna moved into an encouraging phase. 'But you shouldn't despair—you're very beautiful,' and that was only too true. Natasha was one of the most beautiful women she had ever seen—smooth, heavy black hair, a perfect face with a luscious mouth and huge, dark, heavily lashed eyes—long, fine bones in her perfectly proportioned figure . . .

'So *sympathique!*' Natasha made short work of her sixth Martini. 'I *knew* you would be, I felt it as we met. I am very sensitive about these things—it's my Russian blood. You will give Marcus back to me?' It wasn't really a question, it was a command.

'I just couldn't take her seriously,' Anna had been giggling as she later recounted the episode to Isa, and was shocked when her sister refused to see the funny side of it.

'You'd better,' she snapped. 'That *Roshian blod* and the Slavonic temperament's only a blind. She's lethal! Good God, you didn't say yes?'

'N-no,' Anna's eyes glittered. 'I just said she was welcome to try.'

'Anna!' Isa was shocked. 'I know you're up from the country, but do you have to be so damn naïve? You've got Marcus, do you want to lose him? You will if you give that bitch half a chance!'

'Oh,' Anna shrugged as if it meant nothing to her, 'if

he's as easy to lose as that, she's welcome to him. He's not worth having.'

'Stupid!' Isa was growing cross. 'You've got a chance in a million and you're throwing it away by being over-confident—you make me mad!'

'Calm down.' Anna had every part of herself under control—voice, face, hands. It was easy while Marcus was at the other end of the room. She looked around consideringly. 'Doesn't anybody bother about food at these do's? All they've done so far is talk and drink. I'm getting hungry and this buffet looks delicious—Join me?'

'Only a little.' Isa plied the serving spoons sparingly. 'I told you, I can't afford to put on another ounce.'

'That's what I call will power!' Anna heaped her plate.

'Also diplomacy,' came Marcus from behind them. 'Buttering Carl up, a wise move in the circumstances.' He sounded and looked sardonic. 'We're going to be one happy family, Anna and Carl, but never mind about me. I'm only her prospective husband, so I don't count against the cook-housekeeper. As long as she wolfs down everything Carl puts on the table, he'll be her friend and champion for life, while I shall have to grow longer arms to put round her waist.'

Anna looked at her heaped plate—she *had* been over-generous, but she managed to smile sweetly. 'The more there is of me,' she pointed out, 'the more there is to love, and Carl is certainly a treasure to be treated with respect and deference. There aren't many people, even professionals, who could turn out a buffet like this at the drop of a hat.'

'Now you know why I treasure him,' Marcus leered at her. 'He's not only better than any woman, but he's also done a medical course at one time or another. When I told him we were engaged, he said he was quite looking forward to a mistress in the house and possibly, in time, the appearance of a family. He's a fully qualified midwife.'

Anna put down her plate swiftly before it dropped from her nerveless fingers and took a large swallow from her glass of dry white wine. 'I don't believe it,' she said sturdily.

'Neither did I,' his dark eyes mocked her. 'Not until he showed me the certificate from the nursing college he attended. Ask him to show it to you!'

Standing with Marcus in the doorway at nearly two in the morning, Anna waved goodbye to Isa, who was the last guest to leave, and breathed a sigh of relief when at last, Marcus closed the door and they were once more alone. Then the smile which she had maintained through thick and thin since eight o'clock left her face and she rounded on him.

'I do not care,' she remarked icily, 'to have my bottom fondled.'

Marcus leaned back against the wall, very good-looking in a suave way and with his face dark against the crisp whiteness of his evening shirt. 'Then you've changed quite a bit over the past five years,' he was practical and quite shameless. 'You weren't so fussy before—in fact, as I remember, you were all for it.'

Tears of rage sprang into Anna's eyes. 'How dare you!' she shouted, uncaring that Carl, in the kitchen, might hear. 'I was down at heart and disillusioned, I would have thought anybody could have seen that. You should have been a gentleman and not taken advantage of my condition!'

'I was a perfect gentleman,' he retorted. 'My mother always said that a gentleman should try to please a lady, and that's what I did! I congratulate myself I succeeded admirably—I don't think you had anything to complain about, and since we seem to be in the middle of our first row, I think we'd be better in the drawing room. We don't want to disillusion Carl.' His grip on her arm was painful as he forced her through the door and then pushed her to sit on a couch. 'By the way, I shall be going out straight after breakfast tomorrow morning, it's the last meeting with the script writers.'

'Don't you mean you'll be out, smarming round some director and making snide remarks about Isa's latent squint?'

'Not at all,' he smiled, but to Anna it looked more like a smirk of triumph. 'Now you're going to be halfway co-operative, my sweet, I see no reason to draw attention to what's no more than a very minor defect. It's a pity, though—you refusing marriage.'

'Marry you!' she snorted. 'You must have been out of your mind to think I'd ever consider it! Either that or you're so filled with overweening conceit that you think I'd be grateful for your damned condescension. A business arrangement—ha! If you're ever in need of that kind of relationship, just let me know!'

'And you'll oblige, like you did at the motel?'

Anna ground her teeth. 'I'll oblige all right! There's only one thing in the desk, a small address book. Like I said, if you ever—just say the word and I'll start ringing numbers!'

'You've got an evil mind,' Marcus reproved her. 'And while I think about it, Carl will be in that room tomorrow morning bringing in some more pieces of furniture and putting up bookcases—although I don't know why I bother trying to make you comfortable, you're a harridan. Don't offer to help him, he prefers to work alone.'

'Carl seems to be able to do anything,' she snapped. 'I'm seriously thinking of teaching him to type. Once Isa is absolutely sure of this part, I don't think I'll be able to put up with you after all.'

'Contracts,' he reminded her, 'even when they've been signed, can still be broken.'

'But that would mean pretty hefty compensation,' she pointed out triumphantly, and heard his equally triumphant laugh.

'Oh, my naïve little darling, no wonder I decided to marry you! You're so bloody innocent, it's unbelievable! You go and ask Isa whether she wants that part or would she settle for compensation. I know what her answer would be if you don't.'

Anna bit her bottom lip in chagrin. He was perfectly right; Isa wanted—no, that was too mild a word to use—Isa craved that part. It was to be the stepping stone to a great and glorious future. Compensation might pay for the things she wanted for Peggy, but it wouldn't give her any job satisfaction, it wouldn't help her career—on the contrary, it could only damage it.

'How long?' she asked miserably. 'I mean, how long will it take to make this series? A couple of months, perhaps?'

Marcus heaved her up from the couch, put a commiserating arm about her shoulders and led her to the door. 'Listen carefully while I explain. Allow another two months while the script writers and I haggle over how much of my work I'm going to allow them to change before they come up with what I consider an acceptable

version of my book. We've been at it for over a week so
far and we've only managed to cover the first episode.
Then there'll be another month or so for rehearsals.
After that comes the location work and we haven't
decided on a site for that yet, and after that, back to the
studios for the indoor scenes.' He appeared to be working it out and Anna didn't know whether to believe him
or not. He could easily be piling on the agony out of
sheer bloody-mindedness.

'Altogether, my little darling,' he finished, 'with cutting, editing and retakes, I'd say about a year.' And he
smiled at her aggravatingly.

Anna mentally divided his estimate by two, but even
that was too long. She closed her eyes and fought for
control. 'I can't stay here for all that time!' she moaned.

'You can't?' He seemed to find that very amusing.
'But after reading the papers tomorrow morning, I don't
think you'll be exactly welcome back in your old haunts.
Your cavalry twit will choke over his porridge and his
mama will probably read him a stern lecture on the
wisdom of having nothing to do with a fallen woman.
This,' he reached into his pocket and produced a piece of
news-sheet, 'this is what's going to be on sale tomorrow
morning, and as it's quite a popular paper and the gossip
man is quite famous, somebody's bound to have it in
your area. I should imagine it will cause quite a stir in
your little neighbourhood. No, don't tear it,' he admon-
ished as, with hands like claws, she grabbed for it. 'It's a
lovely photograph, instantly recognisable, and the little
caption is out of this world—I wonder who thought that
one up. See—*Trent's Last Case*?—and it goes on to say
my latest is such a honey and I've got this case so badly
that wedding bells must be in the offing.'

Impotent rage consumed her and she let fly with every ounce of her strength. A split second before her hand connected with his face, she knew she'd made a mistake—Marcus wasn't the type to take a slapped face lying down—but it was already too late; she couldn't recall her hand and she gazed horrified as the marks of her fingers began to show red against the swarthiness of his cheek.

The next moment, he had her shoulders in a firm grasp and she was being shaken like a rag doll, and when her head felt as though it was going to fall off, he kissed her.

It was more of an assault than a kiss, she told herself dreamily. His mouth was bruising her lips against her teeth and his hands were going to leave dark marks all over her body. She wished she could remember if this was what it had been like five years ago—had she felt this way then? As if every bone in her body had melted?

Stop enjoying yourself, she told herself sternly, but herself wasn't listening. Herself was having a whale of a time—and without the aid of even one glass of champagne. She collapsed against him bonelessly, and then it was all over. She was standing alone and Marcus was at least two feet away from her and breathing heavily.

'Anna,' he growled it at her through clenched teeth, 'I was taught never to lift my hand to a woman, but you'd try the patience of a saint! Go upstairs while you're still safe!'

Shame at her own weakness jerked her upright and sent a hot flush over her thin cheeks. She felt as though there was a loose-minded trollop inside her who had momentarily got out. Perhaps she'd been wrong about herself all these years. Maybe that episode in the motel had been no champagne-induced happening—maybe she *was* a natural-born trollop.

The shame lent wings to her feet and she was halfway up the first flight of stairs before she stopped running and turned to have the last word, if he killed her for it.

'Damn you!' she shouted defiantly, and then, looking at the back of her hand which she had brushed across her eyes to rid them of the film of tears, 'And damn this mascara as well! Isa swore to me it was waterproof!'

Turning quickly before her eyes had cleared enough to see his face properly, she fled ignominiously up the remaining flights to storm along the corridor and lock herself in her room. Not to stop Marcus getting in, she admitted miserably, but to stop her own self getting out and running back down the stairs to apologise for hitting him.

# CHAPTER SIX

ANNA spent a disturbed night, alternately dozing and
waking to long periods when she tried to find a way out
of the mess she'd fallen in. Finally, just after dawn, she
fell into a heavy sleep and woke at seven, totally unre-
freshed. The bathroom mirror gave back the reflection
of somebody who had been awake all night, so this was
one morning when a quick shower wasn't going to be
enough. Nobody had bothered to tell her when breakfast would be ready, but she was too tired and worried to
care. Instead, she filled the bath with hot water and
flopped in it with a sigh of relief.

The heat of the water helped to relax her taut nerves
and muscles and she lay there, thinking what was best to
do. This wasn't a game any longer. When it had started,
when she had got over the shock of meeting Marcus
again after so long, when he had proposed his little
scheme and—she admitted it to herself—when she had
talked herself into co-operation—then it had all seemed
no more than a jokey game with fringe benefits.

She would be spared the bother of coping with Philip,
and besides, it might be a welcome change from her very
circumscribed existence. She would meet new people,
make new friends—it would be exciting, and excitement
was something of which she had been very short. Yes,
Marcus had made it all sound very attractive and she,
like a fool had fallen for it! But the game had turned sour
on her—it was one she wasn't equipped to play—she

hadn't the right approach. In her place, Isa would have gone to town on this deception, made a meal of it and given a perfect performance—but Isa was a born actress.

Besides, there was another little matter, one which had never entered Anna's calculations. Marcus was too damned attractive and she was falling in love with him—well, if not falling in love, she was beginning to find it very difficult to deny the intense physical attraction he had for her. Part of her wanted out, the sane, reasonable, sensible part, but that part also told her she had to stay and see it through for Isa's sake. The coming year loomed before her like some ghastly mistake, but there was no way round it, no way she could evade it.

Anna knew, deep within her, that she was going to be hurt, but the idea was to keep that hurt to an absolute minimum and, if possible, keep her self-respect. Maybe she'd get used to it! Meanwhile, she was wasting time, and she hauled herself out of the bath and under the cold shower for a few seconds. Cold showers were supposed to be invigorating.

When she returned to her bedroom, it was to find a small tray on the bedside table—Carl, she supposed, delivering morning tea; she hadn't heard him, and while she sipped, she went through the contents of her small suitcase in search of the clean white blouse, underwear and tights she had packed for the return journey to Dorset.

Dressed and with her hair smoothly knotted and her face nicely made up, she went down and through the baize door into the kitchen where Carl was assembling breakfast dishes on a tray.

'May I have mine here?' Carl put her off and she heard the question come out apologetically.

'Breakfast is served in the dining room.' He flattened her pretensions with one glance from marble-like, pale eyes set in an uncommunicative face, picked up the tray and led the way through. At the bottom of the stairs, Marcus joined the little procession, giving Anna a warning glance.

'The kitchen's off limits, it's Carl's province. He won't go into your room, so you keep out of his.'

'That's reasonable,' said the new, self-possessed Anna. 'How are you about other things, like manners? I was always taught to say "Good morning".'

'Oh, that!' He made a great to-do about pulling out her chair for her and seating her before he took a seat directly opposite her. 'Good morning, Anna, I hope you slept well.' He made it sound as though he was reciting it from a well learned lesson. 'I forgot you were so prim— after all, you weren't the first time we met—Will that do for you?'

'Better than nothing,' she said grudgingly as she took a sip of hot, sweet coffee to revive her flagging spirits and began to spoon up cereal. Halfway through the bowlful, she broke the silence.

'I shall have to go home either today or tomorrow, that is, if you're still holding to this trip to France on Saturday. I shall need more clothes.'

Marcus looked up from his bacon and egg. 'Buy them here,' he said tersely.

'Uh-huh,' she shook her head. 'Unnecessary expense,' she explained, beginning to almost enjoy herself. The amount of satisfaction she got out of being unco-operative amazed her—maybe she had to do as she was told for a time, but only in the big things—little matters she could niggle about; so she continued in a cool, remote little voice, addressing the portrait of a woman which hung a few feet above his head on the wall behind him, choosing her words carefully.

'I can see that my employment with you is going to cause me a great deal of strain, therefore I shall try to save as much as possible from the very generous salary you're paying me in order that I can take a long, relaxing holiday when at last I'm free to hand in my notice.'

'If I thought you meant that,' Marcus had paused with a piece of bacon halfway to his mouth, 'I'd sack you this minute. But I don't think you do mean it—you're covering up!'

'Self-deception,' she accused quietly.

'You mean me? Oh no, my girl. I'm looking things straight in the face, not hiding behind a woolly idea of what's nice and what's not nice—which is what you're doing. There's something between us, you know it and so do I, only I'm not pretending it isn't there.'

'Neither am I,' Anna conceded, 'but it's purely animal. I know that, so I shan't give way to it.'

'As you didn't give way to it once before?'

All Anna's cool deserted her. 'How *dare* you!' she almost shrieked. 'How dare you keep throwing that in my face! I've told you before, I didn't know what I was doing . . .'

'. . . And the time may come again when you don't know what you're doing,' Marcus pointed out. 'Which is why I don't think this engagement's all that satisfactory. The way I see it, you've been living in a pool of guilt for years and it's warped you—if it happened again, you'd start thinking of yourself as a fallen woman.'

'It won't happen again,' she said stormily. 'That was a

one-off occasion. I'm not a romantic teenager any longer, I've learned my lesson.'

'Please yourself,' he shrugged, 'but remember, I've offered . . .'

'. . . And your magnanimity so overcomes me that I *have* to refuse,' she was tart and biting. 'As you said, I've lived with it for years, I hardly ever think about it now—and I'm *not* warped! I'm very well adjusted and I'd like the day off to collect . . .'

'No!' He said obdurately. 'I want that outline in type before we leave for France so I can get started on the first chapter when we arrive.'

'And that's the "rest" you talked about?'

'My very dear little fiancée, getting the right words in the right order down on paper *is* my idea of a rest, so go and do some shopping while I battle with the script-writers; then we can make a start.'


Through the window of the malodorous old taxi, Anna watched the whitewashed, blue-roofed, blue-shuttered Villa des Pins appear as the uphill road curved. Sheltered by a stand of scrub pines in the curve of the hill overlooking Agde, it was a welcome sight. Everybody said this was the hottest early June on record and the inside of the taxi was unbearable, stuffy and smelly. She paid off the driver at the gate, adding a few extra francs as a tip, and almost ran up the path with the sun beating down on her uncovered head like blows from a white-hot hammer. Within the porch, the door stood open invitingly and she fled through it, to pause in the cool dimness of the hallway, blinking while her eyes adjusted to what seemed like semi darkness. Marcus's voice came out of the gloom and he loomed over her like some dark angel—a darker shadow against the dimness.

'Where the hell have you been—Carl's been back for hours!' and he wasn't sounding very good-tempered. 'I thought I told you . . .'

'. . . You told me I could have Carl take me in to Agde,' she reminded him tartly, trying to be oblivious to the harsh grate of his voice. 'You said Carl would take me—which he did—but you didn't say anything about making him wait for me while I did my shopping. That's because you treat him as if he was some sort of robot! You've simply no idea of how hot it was down there or how tiring it would be for him. So I sent him back and got a taxi when I was ready to come home.' She raised her nose several degrees in the air. 'I grew out of nursemaids years ago!'

'And what would have happened if you'd dropped on a taxi driver who couldn't speak English?' he rasped. 'You could have caused an international incident, the way you speak French—it's pathetic!'

'I would have used sign language or drawn a map,' she retorted, gritting her teeth. 'Maybe my French isn't much . . .'

'. . . It's not,' he broke in. 'It sounds more like Chinese!'

Anna's hands crisped on the handles of the plastic carrier she was holding and her eyes sparkled with wrath. 'We don't all have your advantages,' she said haughtily. 'Some of us live quite ordinary lives, we haven't lived raggy sorts of lives in Montmartre apartments while we turned out masterpieces, neither have we had the sort of coaching in the language which you had—individual tuition on a one-to-one basis. Actually,

I think I managed rather well, and I'm certainly not helpless. Furthermore . . .'

'There's more?'

'There certainly is,' she became lofty. 'You gave me the afternoon off, so it's none of your business what I do with it, and,' at this point her loftiness and haughty air deserted her and she descended to plain nastiness—she'd enjoyed her shopping expedition and he was taking all the pleasure out of it for her—'and if I don't want your tame gorilla hanging around, I won't have him!'

'Carl is not a gorilla,' he snapped.

'No,' she conceded. 'I'm sorry I said that—he's a very nice person, and how he's put up with you all these years, I can't imagine. He must have the patience of a saint.'

'Unlike you, Anna, he appreciates a good employer.'

'A good employer!' Her voice rose several decibels. 'Is that what you call yourself? Let me tell you, a good employer wouldn't wake the whole household at two in the morning and get them both downstairs—one to type and the other to make coffee, just because *you* couldn't sleep!'

She was putting on a very brave show but when he took a threatening pace towards her, she backed up against the wall, holding her carrier bag as though it was some kind of shield, but he followed relentlessly and his hand closed over her mouth, silencing her.

'Keep your voice down,' he growled. 'I know we're alone here, but it's time you learned a little self-control—and don't say you're short-tempered from lack of sleep. I didn't ask you to do anything this morning, did I? I sent you back to bed when we'd finished what I wanted to do and I told you to have a lie-in, didn't I?' He removed his hand just in time and her teeth closed with a snap on thin air instead of on the fleshy bit at the base of his thumb. She opened her mouth to tell him more of what she thought about his high-handed behaviour, but suddenly decided on discretion rather than valour.

'I can't sleep to order,' she grumbled. 'I've never been used to sleeping during the day.'

'Then adjust,' he rapped out, 'and don't be so bloody-minded about it—it won't happen all that often.' Abruptly, his tone changed. 'Bought something nice?'

'Toothpaste,' she evaded. She didn't relish displaying her purchases to his cynical gaze. There was a new dress of cream silk in her favourite shirtwaister style, a filmy scarf in emerald green and some gloves which matched it exactly—those weren't too bad, but under them was a very small packet which contained underwear, the kind she'd always wanted and never bought—gauzy silk with lace, very French, and she was shy about it.

Marcus surveyed her frantic fingers clutching at the bag and grinned understandingly. 'Rather a big bag for toothpaste?'

'It's the jumbo, economy size,' Anna turned innocent-looking eyes on him and smiled sweetly. 'Mint-flavoured, and I use a lot of it, so it works out cheaper this way. I hope you haven't waited tea for me?'

'Carl's making it now.' He stepped back to let her pass him and hastened her on her way with a pat on her derrière. 'Hurry up, my little love, I've missed you this afternoon.'

'And I've missed you,' she cooed back adoringly as she mounted the stairs. 'Agde was a desert without you, and I did so want you there to share my cream cakes.'

'Then you won't want any of Carl's mandarin gateau.

Pity! He made it specially for you.' Now that her eyes had adjusted to the cool dimness of the hallway, she could see Marcus's smile, a slightly teasing one and quite unlike his usual sardonic grin.

'I've always got room for Carl's gateau,' she reproved. 'Somebody has to give him a bit of encouragement when he goes to all that trouble—he doesn't get much from you!'

'Cream's fattening,' he warned. 'You'll get plump.'

Anna's face assumed the sort of expression which indicated she had made a discovery. 'You mean that's why you don't eat his confections? Yes,' she pursed her lips judiciously, 'very wise of you—you wouldn't live up to your image, not if you had a middle-aged spread and at your time of life!' and with a delighted smile and a choked-back giggle, she fled up the remaining stairs.

That was how it was between them, a biting, uneasy kind of relationship in which she had only her swift tongue to counter what she called his sledge-hammer tactics, and she used her tongue to its best advantage to save herself from being overwhelmed and reduced to a cipher. For bluntness and tearing sarcasm, Marcus had no equal—a great many of his remarks hit and hurt her, but she had a year to serve until Isa was assured in her career and she was determined to hold out no matter what the cost.

She sighed as she stepped under a cold shower to rid her nostrils of the various odours of the taxi—garlic, fish, a stale vegetable smell she couldn't identify—and she concentrated instead on the taxi driver's easy flow of conversation in heavily accented but perfectly understandable English, and from that, went on to her present situation, which was dull in the extreme.

The villa was beautiful, not a modern creation but old and gracious yet with every modern convenience, even a small swimming pool, but so far, after almost a week, this was all she had seen of France, and she had hoped for so much more. Roman France was just around the corner, she'd looked it up on the map—Nîmes with its aqueduct, Arles and the Alyscamps—Fréjus—the Camargue . . .

By the time Anna was ready to go down to the patio for tea, she was obsessed with a burning sense of injustice. All work and no play made for a drab existence, and so far she had worked, typing until her fingers nearly fell off, while Marcus constantly changed his mind about the right order for the right words which were to make a first chapter which would hit the public with the impact of a charging bull elephant. At first, she had tried to alter the finished typescript, but after two days she simply tore up the offending sheets and started afresh.

Down on the patio, Marcus was waiting for her, looking incredibly cool and suave while she, fresh from a cold shower and stiff with talcum, was already feeling sticky. Her eyes slid over him, not with love but with envy and then were veiled beneath her lashes as he deliberately let his roam over her.

'You're looking very cool and sedate,' he gestured at her green and white candy-striped cotton dress—one she had bought in London with the south of France in mind—and she wished she had put on the little matching jacket which would have covered her shoulders and concealed the narrow straps which were their only covering.

'Thank you.' He had said she looked sedate, so she

would be sedate. 'But I think we'd be cooler if we had tea in the *salon*.'

'You don't care for alfresco meals?' Marcus raised an eyebrow. 'There's no pleasing some people! We thought you'd prefer to eat outside—most of our visitors do. They say it's a nice change from England. A June night, a full moon and dinner on the patio by candlelight—very romantic! What more could you want?'

'A can of fly spray beside every plate and a large piece of mosquito netting,' Anna answered swiftly. 'Is that what's going to happen tonight?'

'No,' he leered at her mockingly as she handed him a cup of tea and proffered a plate of thinly cut sandwiches. 'In view of the bother I caused you both last night, dragging you from your beds and because of the noble way you suffered in silence, I've decided you both deserve a treat. Carl is having the evening off and I'm taking you out for dinner. When Carl comes to collect the tea-things, he'll probably thank you for the kind thought.'

'Thank me?' Anna looked her surprise. 'Why should he do that? It wasn't my idea.'

'No, but I let him think it was.' Marcus looked innocent. 'I was sure you'd have thought of it eventually, so I just mentioned it in passing. It's important you and Carl get on and I'm fostering a good relationship between you—the two most important people in my life.'

'Oh!' Anna cut herself a large piece of gateau to cover the awkward moment and give herself time to think. Dinner out wasn't without its advantages. 'So much thought for others!' she was sweetly waspish. 'I hardly like to trespass on your good nature, but since you're so insistent, I accept with pleasure.'

'Good girl!' Marcus complimented her, and reached out a hand to clasp her fingers. 'Are you at last coming to terms with our bargain?'

'Mmm.' She removed her hand swiftly from beneath his. No matter how she schooled her mind, she couldn't conquer and kill the physical attraction he had for her. The touch of his fingers was like a mild shock from a bare electric wire and it took a great deal of self-control not to show how deeply she was disturbed. A man of distinction—the second line of that damn song, and so applicable to him. He stood out, head and shoulders above any other man—dear lord, let her not fall in love with him! Let her not be led astray by warm nights, moonlight and the close relationship which was developing between them, as she had once been led astray by a lot of champagne and what she'd thought was a broken heart.

'Mmm,' she heard herself repeat the murmur and erected her barrier against him, the only one she had—her tongue. 'I've been thinking about that. A year isn't so long, not really, and you're paying me well, that is when I see the colour of your money . . .'

'You'll get paid at the end of the month,' he assured her. 'We'll be back in England by then. Which reminds me, prepare yourself for a few sticky moments, because nobody's going to believe in your purity and they'd laugh in your face if you tried to convince them of it. You may be my fiancée-cum-secretary, but you try telling them you're not my mistress!'

'You've forgotten Carl,' she reminded him triumphantly.

'Oh no, I haven't,' he leered at her salaciously. 'You can't quote Carl as a chaperon—Carl's unique. He hears nothing, knows nothing and says nothing!'

Anna bit her lip in vexation. 'I wonder why people have such evil minds?' she murmured as, despite the heat of the sun, she could feel herself growing cold—as though she was freezing right through to her bones. The freezing process helped, though, because when Marcus laughed aloud, she found she was able to put a forkful of gateau into her mouth and sigh with pleasure at the taste.

'Your own fault, my love,' he jeered. 'I told you I wasn't satisfied with an engagement, but you wouldn't trust me. You seemed to think I had some personal motive for our marriage, while actually I was only thinking of you.'

'How very noble of you!' She contorted her face into a wintry smile. 'But you could hardly expect me to think you were thinking of me, could you—I haven't known you long, but what I know makes me suppose you never think of anybody but Marcus Trent. Anyway, I suppose it'll be a seven-day wonder and I'll cope with it. Being labelled as your mistress is much the same as being your live-in fiancée, the two things are much of a muchness.'

'I don't like messy personal relationships,' Marcus snapped.

Anna gazed down at her plate—she had eaten her piece of cake right down to the last crumb without realising it and without tasting a thing, and she carefully cut herself another piece. She was filled with self-admiration—her hands weren't shaking, her voice was steady—she was surprised she could speak normally after the shock she'd had, there wasn't a tremor or an ounce of expression in her tones.

'A mess of your own making,' she pointed out icily but

without rancour, as though all of this was happening to somebody else—that she wasn't involved at all.

'Oh no,' he said callously. 'Your mess, not mine. I was perfectly willing to do the correct thing, remember? You were the obstinate one. There's one consolation, although you probably won't look at it that way . . .'

'What's that?' Head down over her plate, her eyes fixed on a mound of cream topped with orange sections, Anna didn't see the gleam of triumph in his eyes.

'You won't be able to claim you're being hanged for a sheep rather than a lamb,' he pointed out jeeringly. 'Your lamb days ended five years ago—and now,' he rose to his feet and towered over her, 'you can go and have a little rest before you start dressing. We ought to leave here at seven, I've booked a table at a place in Frontignan and it'll take us at least an hour to get there.' He waited a second or so for her reply, but when she failed to even raise her head, he snarled something under his breath and strode into the villa without a backward glance.

Anna finished counting the orange sections and took a deep breath. She felt battered and bruised all over, and now he was gone, she was breathing too quickly, almost gulping for air, and there was a clammy dew of perspiration on her forehead. Marcus had set out deliberately to shock her, and he'd succeeded beyond his wildest dreams, but she'd covered up very well, she thought. She hadn't cringed or whimpered, not even at his last remark, which had bitten deep into her self-esteem. He still didn't know he could hurt her and—her mouth firmed—he never would!

She climbed the stairs wearily to the privacy of her room, and once behind the locked door, the ice melted and she sank on to the bed and let her held-back tears flow. Being a martyr wasn't a pleasant task, but if she kept her mind on Isa and Peggy, thought of nothing else but their welfare, maybe it wouldn't be so bad. Unlike Marcus, she cared what people thought of her. Marcus—the thought of him made her push her face into the pillow, trying to shut him out. Was a physical attraction the same thing as love? She didn't think so and she hoped not; to be in love with him would be the final blow—one from which she suspected she wouldn't recover.

Anna had only the two evening dresses and she hauled them both out of the wardrobe to examine them for suitability. She dismissed the black which she had worn to the party, it was a little too dressy for a quiet meal out and it would need a stole or some other covering. In any case, she suspected that in it she didn't look the part of a secretary. But the other, a loose, bronzy green caftan with some gold embroidery round the neckline and sleeves, would be ideal. It had a peasant, unsophisticated look and she thought she'd be comfortable in it. She flicked at her face with a powderpuff, smeared on a little rusty red lipstick and with her chin high, she went down to the *salon*.

'Nice dress,' Marcus greeted her. 'Was that what you were so busy buying this afternoon?'

'No.' She crossed to the long window, now unshuttered, and pulled back the filmy curtain to peer out into the gathering darkness—a stupid thing to do and which was rewarded by a smack in the face from a big night moth lured in by the lights. Hastily she let the curtain drop. 'This afternoon I bought a cream silk shirtwaister, an emerald green scarf and some matching gloves—

this,' she indicated the bronzy green with a sweep of her hand, 'I believe you bought this for me in London. It came via Isa for that ghastly party.'

'But you wore black.'

'Umm.' She accepted a glass of sherry and took a sip, hoping it would give her courage. 'But you don't know Isa very well, do you? She loves spending money, especially other people's money. You told her to get me a dress and, so I could have a choice, she bought two. I meant to send one of them back, but now I'm glad I didn't. I think I'm going to earn them. I've made up my mind I'm going to get something out of this damn charade you have me playing. No, not that,' as his eyes strayed to the ruby glowing on her finger. 'You can have that back any old time—now, if you like.'

'But I don't like,' he told her gravely. 'We've so few trappings of respectability and we might meet somebody I know.'

'Big deal!' snorted Anna. 'Whose reputation are you supposed to be saving, yours or mine?'

'Yours, of course, my pet.' He put an arm about her waist and led her out to the car. 'You've got that lovely, untouched look about you despite your murky past. Keep looking doe-eyed and demure and we might get away with it!'

'How gorgeous!' Anna forgot about being self-contained and withdrawn as she gazed around the restaurant. 'Is this one of those "serious" eating places?' She didn't really have to ask the question, she'd known as she stepped into the dining room. The waiter who took them to their table wasn't obsequious, neither did he proffer a menu. Instead he loaded the centre of their table with a yellow glazed bowl of pink prawns in the shell, another brown bowl containing chunks of salt bread and a board on which stood a large block of butter. After that, he brought a large bottle of cooled white wine and left them to their own devices.

'Very serious,' Marcus grimaced. 'We don't even have a choice about what we eat. Wine?'

'Please.' She shelled a prawn and took a tentative bite at it. 'This is salty and smells of the sea.' She watched the wineglass mist as he poured and took a grateful sip while her eyes strayed to the window and the dark lake which lay outside, the dark water glimmering in the moon light.

Four pieces of salt bread later and with the block of butter diminished by half and a mountain of prawn shells on her plate, Anna gave a sigh of pure satisfaction and gulped at her second glass of wine. 'That was lovely, I wouldn't have missed it for the world.' Somehow, all the stress and hurt of the afternoon had vanished, she felt warm and content, even happy, and Marcus was being very good company—he hadn't snarled once!

'Good Lord!' He smiled at her across the table. 'Have I managed to do something to please you at last?'

'Oh, don't spoil it, please,' she implored. 'I'm enjoying myself. Couldn't we forget the nasty bits, just for this evening? I'd like to have one nice thing to remember.'

Ceremoniously, Marcus picked up her hand from where it was lying on the table and raised her fingers to his lips. 'As my lady wishes,' and then he spoiled the romantic gesture by wrinkling his nose. 'You smell of prawns,' and he pushed a finger bowl towards her.

Anna giggled at the absurdity and dabbled her fingers

in the water. 'It makes a change from typewriter rib-
bons,' she said demurely. 'What comes next?' as the
waiter came with fresh plates and a smoking dish.

'*Langouste à la sêtoise*, a speciality of this restaurant.
It's rather like *homard à l'américain*, only it's made with
crawfish and the sauce contains more garlic and toma-
toes,' Marcus chuckled. 'Carl's been here, trying to get
the recipe—he cooks it exactly as they told him, but it
never turns out quite right. He says it's because he can't
get hold of really fresh crawfish in London, but I think
this deserves something better than white wine, so will
you share a bottle of champagne with me?' He flung
down the challenge, and with a definite sparkle in her
eyes, Anna picked it up.

'It will be a pleasure, Mr Trent!'

The car sped back through the darkness, past Sête and
Agde and up the hill to the villa, to turn in through the
gates and come to rest outside the door. 'Home,
sweetheart.' Marcus gave her a nudge and Anna slipped
out of a contented doze to walk up the two steps to the
door with his arm about her.

'Aren't you going to put the car away?' she asked
sleepily.

'It's locked, it won't come to any harm.' In the darkness, his voice came deep and a little husky.

'Such idleness!' she reproved as he pushed the door
open for her and she walked through into the hall. The
old house still held some of the warmth of the day and
smelled deliciously of beeswax and lavender, and in the
dimness of the hall, it seemed quite natural to her to drift
into Marcus's arms and lift her face to his.

'Saying goodnight and thank you in the time-

honoured way?' Marcus sounded as though he was
teasing and Anna didn't bother to reply. The attraction—she couldn't be bothered to decide whether it was
physical or mental—was back in full force and she felt
herself melting against him.

'If you like,' she murmured, and when his mouth
found hers, it was like coming home after a long journey.
She sighed against his lips and her hands slid about his
neck and she gave a little sigh of content when she felt his
hand on her breast. That seemed perfectly natural as
well as she was drowning in bliss. The fighting was
over—there hadn't really been anything to fight about.
This was what she wanted, had been wanting all her
life—this was love.

'Anna—' she hardly recognised Marcus's voice, it was
so thick and there was a tremble at the back of it. 'Anna,
I want you.'

It was like a douche of cold water in her face—not
'Anna, I love you' but 'Anna, I *want* you'. The caressing
fingers at her breast were no longer caressing, they were
an invasion, and the touch of his mouth wasn't sweet any
more but hot and demanding. It was as though she had
held heaven in her hands and after the delight, found
only a handful of dirt.

The softness left her body and she stiffened in his
arms, wrenching her mouth from his. 'Let me go!' She
thought she shouted it, but all she heard was a savage
whisper as she fought to free herself.

'What's the matter?' he snarled, as savage as she. 'Are
you one of those bloody teases? Hell, we were doing all
right . . .' His arm tightened about her and his hand
gripped painfully at the soft stuff of her dress and the soft
body beneath it.

'Let me go!' she repeated it as she fought against him and when she was finally free, she fled to the bottom stair where she turned round, anger and disappointment making her voice shrill as she shouted at him all the hurtful things she could think of.

'Swine!' Her eyes slitted and glittered green. 'Did you think I was that easy? I'm not nineteen now and I've learned quite a lot since then. It takes more than a good dinner and a couple of glasses of champagne to buy me nowadays, and a few kisses and a pathetic "Anna, I want you" don't have any effect on me. It'll take a hell of a lot more than that to get me into your bed or for me to allow you in mine. I'm fussy, you see. I mightn't be exactly in mint condition myself, but I draw the line at men like you—sophisticated lechers!'

She was too angry for tears, but the anger was for herself—for being so easily stirred, for giving way so easily, and she silently thanked heaven for coming to her senses before it was too late. In another minute, she'd have been telling him she loved him.

Anna didn't know who she hated most, Marcus or herself, but the hate was there, spurring her on so that she mounted only two stairs before she turned on him again. 'Don't just stand there looking at me as though I'm out of my mind,' she wasn't shouting any more but muttering violently. 'Here, catch!' and she tore the ring from her finger and hurled it at him. 'That puts us right back at the beginning. I'm a typist from now on, I'm not a live-in anything, and I'll thank you to remember it!'

'Anna!' Marcus was harsh and frightening so that she ran up the stairs, but he was right behind her when she reached the door of her room and his hand was tight on hers as she struggled with the doorknob. His hands gripped her shoulders and she closed her eyes in fright, visions of rape dancing through her brain. It was as if he could read her mind.

'Don't look at me like that,' he gave her shoulders a shake which rattled the teeth in her head. 'Rape's not in my line, I like my women willing. But if you think you're walking out on me now, you can think again. We made a bargain and I'm holding you to it. Here,' he thrust the ring into her fingers, 'that goes back on for a start. If anybody's going to walk out, it'll be me, not you—not until I say you can, and I haven't said that yet.'

'Of course it'd be you who walked out,' she flared, a bitter note at the back of her anger. 'You couldn't stand the humiliation of being publicly rejected, it would be bad for your image as the great Lothario. All right, I'll save your precious image—after all, it wouldn't do for anybody to find out that there's one woman who isn't willing to fall into bed with you . . . You have a reputation to maintain. Love 'em and leave 'em, Marcus. We mustn't let them see what's behind the façade, must we?'

Marcus's hand was on the latch, the door swung open and she was hustled through and nearly hurled on the bed. 'Stay there where you're safe,' he grated. 'Yes, you're perfectly safe, I wouldn't touch you—you're warped!'

'And if I am?' she shouted at his retreating back. 'Whose fault is that? Who made me the way I am?'

# CHAPTER SEVEN

ANNA hadn't expected to sleep well, but when she woke in the morning, it was with the feeling that it would have been better if she'd stayed awake all night. She felt much worse than when she'd gone to bed, but then she had been buoyed up by anger and a sense of acute injustice— now, in addition to tiredness, there was a cold clutching in her stomach at the thought of facing Marcus after last night's scene.

A hot shower hardly helped at all, and she stared miserably at the reflected wreck of her face. Before this, she had always managed with a dab of foundation and a smear of lipstick, but since Marcus had re-entered her life, she needed to spend more and more time each morning while she covered up dark stains beneath her eyes and added a little colour to her wan cheeks.

But face him she had to, and cowering in her bedroom was only delaying the inevitable confrontation. She chose her most mannish white cotton shirt—one which buttoned up to a black bow at the severely cut collar; a thin, straight black skirt, dark tights and flat sandals, and she scraped her hair back a little more tightly than usual. All this, including the extra layer of tinted foundation and the hardly noticeable lipstick, was an armour. Enclosed within it, she could be coolly professional, and she would *not* lose her temper, no matter what Marcus said or how he treated her!

Her good intention lasted just as long as it took her to

go downstairs into the *salon* and seat herself at the breakfast table. Marcus was already there and he paused with a forkful of scrambled eggs halfway to his mouth.

'Good morning, Anna.' It was as though she'd never yelled dreadful things at him—never thrown his ring in his face. 'You're late!'

Anna kept her cool. 'Late night.' If he could pretend last night had never happened, so could she. 'Did you need me earlier?'

'No, but Isa did.' His mocking smile was back in place, deriding her workmanlike appearance. 'She was on the phone at some unearthly hour this morning and she wanted to speak to you.'

Anna helped herself to a cup of coffee, anything solid would have stuck in her throat and choked her. 'Then why wasn't I wakened?' she demanded fiercely, her eyes beginning to glitter.

'Because I decided you needed your sleep,' he replied blandly, 'although,' once again his eyes flicked over her, leaving no detail of her appearance unsurveyed, 'it doesn't look as though it's done you any good—or is it that get-up you're wearing? You look like a sour spinster and not a day under thirty!'

Anna ignored this. Marcus was very good at personal comments, each one hit where it would hurt most. 'What did she want?'

He shrugged. 'Don't ask me—I didn't ask her. All I know is that she's arriving in Béziers at noon, so hurry up with your breakfast or we'll be late meeting the train.'

Her hand clenched tightly on her coffee cup and despite all her good resolutions, Anna could feel aggravation building up to an unendurable pitch within her. 'You could have asked her,' she spat. 'There must be something wrong for her to be coming out here. You're being your usual lousy self, getting back at me because I wouldn't go to bed with you last night! You knew I'd worry, you *wanted* me to worry—anything so you could mend your damn ego! Isa wouldn't come all this way by train for no reason at all . . .'

'She flew out to Toulouse yesterday afternoon,' he corrected, 'booked herself into a hotel for the night, so the train journey's only from Toulouse. No sweat—and she was phoning from the hotel, a paybox, I think, she said she'd only got enough change for a short call. As for your refusing to go to bed with me, I can't remember asking.'

Hot colour swept over her face, but she refused to lower her eyes. 'I know a proposition when I hear it,' she muttered.

'You've had so many?' The severity of his face broke up, changing to a devilish glee, and she had the grace to look slightly ashamed.

'Enough!' and she took refuge behind her coffee cup. 'All the same . . .'

'You'd better finish your breakfast and change,' it was an order. 'I'm not taking you out with me in that prison uniform—and,' he finished his own coffee and rose from the table, passing behind her and giving a little tug at her hair, 'loosen that a bit, my dear, you look like a skinned rabbit!'

When the door had closed behind him, Anna poured herself another cup of coffee and tried to chew at a piece of toast but it stuck in her throat so she abandoned it. Meanwhile, the cogs of her mind creaked and groaned as they meshed and turned, oh, so slowly. She felt as though she no longer had the power to think in a straight line. Isa was coming here and Marcus was agreeable—that was a minor miracle for a start, him allowing his precious privacy to be invaded.

Or maybe it wasn't a miracle at all. Perhaps Marcus had given up on her—maybe he'd decided to take up his option on Isa. Anna had no idea of the physical needs of men, but they'd been here for a week—a week during which Marcus had kept his nose firmly to the grindstone, and despite his abrupt, almost callous manner, she didn't think he was undersexed. A storm of jealousy shook her at the thought of Isa and Marcus together, but it died quickly as she realised the implications.

Isa had said she was willing if it would give her career a boost, it would mean nothing to her—just a means to an end, but if that happened, Anna would be free. The bargain would no longer hold, and she wondered why freedom looked so uninviting.

'Darling Anna!' Isa descended from the train, a dainty vision in delphinium blue silk. 'My, but you're looking nice!' Her blue eyes took in every detail of the cream silk shirtwaister, the emerald green chiffon scarf, gloves and Anna's strappy, high-heeled sandals. 'Much better, you're at last developing a dress sense.'

Anna suffered a very light kiss—emotion was never allowed to spoil Isa's make-up—and detached her sister's arms from about her neck, her nose wrinkling at the strength of Isa's flowery perfume. 'What are you doing here?' she demanded. 'Has something gone wrong with the TV thing—and where's Peggy, and my dog?'

'Of course something's gone wrong,' Isa snorted, then wasted time beckoning to a blue-clad porter to load her three matching suitcases on to a trolley. 'Oh, not with the film, that's all right, and Peggy's hidden. About your dog, though—I'm sorry, love, but I haven't had a moment to spare. He's still with your vet—I rang up and they're keeping him till you get back.'

'Then if it's not the film, not Peggy or the dog . . .'

'Philip, stupid!' Isa allowed herself a small, quick frown and almost stamped a daintily shod foot. 'Come along, follow the porter or we'll lose my bags. Has Marcus got the car outside?'

'Mmm.' Anna remained stationary, despite Isa's tug at her arm. 'I'm not moving until I know what this is all about.'

Isa sighed and began her explanation as they walked slowly up the platform. 'The pompous prig! Somehow he got to know about the buyer for the house—yes, we have one and he's offering quite a good price—Well, my dear husband arrived on my doorstep yesterday morning—all is forgiven and I'm to be received back into the fold—I ask you, have you ever heard such damn cheek? I refused, of course, but you know Philip—he didn't even listen to me, so when he'd gone, I hid Peggy with some friends, threw a few things in a suitcase and ran for cover. There was a cancellation on the afternoon flight to Toulouse, so I took it, and here I am—and Philip can ring that doorbell till he's blue in the face, there's nobody there to answer it. For heaven's sake, say you're glad to see me, I'm beginning to feel unwanted! But have you ever heard of such unmitigated gall—Philip forgiving *me*!'

'Easily,' Anna snorted. 'Marcus said that's what he would do.'

'What's Marcus got to do with it?' Isa raised a supercilious eyebrow.

'Nothing,' Anna shrugged, 'but I believe he wrote the book!'

'Don't be enigmatic, darling,' Isa scolded gently. 'Look, I'm sorry, I didn't want to intrude into your love-nest, but honestly, I couldn't think of anywhere else, and another session with Philip would have driven me out of my mind! He started slating you—how you'd deceived him, how you'd degenerated from a nice girl into a sex-mad freak—or was it that you'd always been a secret sexoholic? I can't remember—after a while, I stopped listening. I won't get in your way, I promise, and I shan't say a word. Whatever the relationship, it's good for you, you've developed a bit of style.'

Anna heard what Isa was saying, although she wasn't really listening. Her sister dodged from one point to another as each one occurred to her, which made her difficult to follow, but most of it got through—Isa's pitch and superlative diction ensured that! Anna was left with a mental picture of Isa and Philip—Philip laying down the law with heavy emphasis on the 'do nots'; all culled from his mother who had done some nifty mental gymnastics, not only to change her opinion of the disastrous marriage but also to find good reasons for doing so. Of course, there would have been no mention of Isa's little fortune now that the house was to be sold, and certainly, Philip's plans for the new place on Wareham Heath would be left in the background.

Anna thought somebody should bring it up. 'Philip's after the money,' she murmured—a bit out of place since Isa was chattering about TV commercials.

'Don't I know it!' Isa caught on at once. 'He's already spending it for me, and you, you fallen woman, you with your feet of clay, you man-hungry tigress who masquerades as a little pussycat—you're not to have a penny in case you spend it on your fancy men and riotous living.' The walk up the length of the platform had degenerated into a crawl as Isa kept halting to give emphasis to what she was saying. 'Honest, he's such a pathetic creature, I almost feel sorry for him— driven by Mummy and such a good, obedient gee-gee!'

Anna pointed out gravely that they'd lost the porter. 'Let's get on, we can talk later.'

From the gate, she could see Marcus leaned against the car, the porter was pulling his empty trolley away with one hand while he stuffed some francs in his pocket with the other and Isa smiled sunnily at the sight. 'Isn't he marvellous—Marcus, your man. You can leave him to do anything and,' she slid a glance to Anna, 'he's good to look at as well.'

Anna sniffed, '*Not* my man, Isa,' and then she remembered the pretence and thought she'd better keep it up. 'We're only engaged . . .'

'Then you're a very slow worker,' Isa chided. 'In your shoes, I'd have something better than that after a week alone with him!' and she advanced on Marcus, her arms stretched to clasp him and her flowerlike face raised for a welcoming kiss.

'Darling,' she cooed, 'how lovely to see you both, and what have you been doing to my little sister? You've turned a business type lady into a woman!' The kiss was featherlight and when she stepped back from it, 'I hope you've burned every one of those ghastly "working" clothes she wears!'

'I'm saving the bonfire for you to light.' Anna saw him smile down at Isa—nothing saturnine or sardonic, 'and

I've a comprehensive mental list of all the items to be destroyed.'

And I'm one of them, Anna thought. I'm to be reduced to a smoking ruin for your pleasure. But she didn't say it, instead she smiled sweetly and played her part with all the appearance of enthusiasm.

'Give me the list,' she hoped she sounded sophisticatedly cool, 'and I'll provide the combustible material. I'll even stoke the fire while you two dance round it!'

Marcus hustled them into the car, Isa at the back and Anna beside him, saying that the sum of two women in the back of a car was continuous chatter and he required silence while he was driving. Anna looked at him out of the corner of her eye—didn't he know that she and Isa never chattered? Small talk was Isa's province, but Anna only provided the impetus for it by putting in a word now and then to keep her volatile sister going.

'What a super place!' From her seat in the rear, Isa had her first glimpse of the villa—the blue shutters, like closed eyes, giving the house a blank and secretive look. 'What's hidden behind those blank walls? The whole place reminds me of a mystery story I once read.'

'Ask Anna, my dear,' Marcus gave his fiancée a leer as he threw the words over his shoulder. 'She's the secretive one. You know me—what I do, I do in the full light of day,' and one of his hands left the wheel to come to rest on Anna's knee and his thumb stroked caressingly.

There was nothing Anna could do about it, not with Isa in the back seat, her senses alert to analyse each word and gesture. She felt a sweet discomfort as something dissolved in her stomach and released a warm, seductive wave which swamped her, but fortunately they had arrived and Carl was there, morose and with his bald head shining in the sunlight. Anna scrambled out without waiting for her door to be opened—glad to get away from the nebulous thing which threatened to destroy her as it reduced all her old values to zero.

'Darling!' Isa paused in the corridor on the way to her room, flinging a quick glance over her shoulder to see that she and Anna were alone. 'Darling, you've got it made—Marcus is all yours, and it shows! Wait till I tell them back in London—our dear Natasha will gnash her teeth in fury. She failed! And then a country mouse walked in and scooped the pool. He's rich—he's famous . . .'

'A real man of distinction,' Anna murmured, trying to keep the bitterness out of her voice. 'Don't you think it's too much like a fairy story? Use your head, Isa! I'm a country bumpkin, a novelty, that's all.' She wasn't so much telling Isa as telling herself, dragging the romantic curtain aside so that the plain, unvarnished facts showed plainly—pushing the knife into her own breast and giving it a twist for good measure. 'And there's nothing "going on",' she added. 'You'd be surprised at the purity of our lives!'

Isa reacted as Marcus said everybody would react. She laughed, a gay, unbelieving chuckle, and then enquired which door belonged to the bathroom.

Anna left her, head down in a suitcase, deciding what to wear, and went back to the patio where Marcus was slouched in a lounger, gulping thirstily from a can of beer. He raised his head, took one look at her face and burst into sardonic laughter.

'She didn't believe you!' he jeered over the rim of the beer can. 'You won't like it, my sweet, but I can't resist saying "I told you so'!"

'Stop it!' Anna's nerves felt as though they were strung as tight as piano wires. 'OK, I didn't believe you, but you were right.'

'I always am.' He put down the can with a thump and came across to put an arm about her waist. 'But we don't want her to know the truth, do we? That your fair name is being sullied for her sake. It might damage her self-confidence, and that would play hell with her performance. She's the star, she has to carry this series and if she slips up, it'll be a flop. So, we give the impression of an ideally happy engaged couple, maybe or maybe not having a trial run—all of which she'll misunderstand completely. Sorry, Anna, but your reputation's gone for a Burton, because you know Isa isn't going to go back and tell them we're being old-fashioned and virtuous. Half her triumph will lie in telling everybody we're in the throes of something passionate—a much more exciting story. Why is she here anyway?'

'Philip,' Anna wriggled, but his arm remained firm about her waist, 'you know!' She grew exasperated. 'You wrote the book before it even happened.'

'A reconciliation, now that she can fund his new venture? Lord, she'll be a fool if she falls for that.'

'Pressures,' Anna said darkly. 'You ought to know about those, you clamp them on whenever it suits you. There's Peggy, Isa won't give her up, and if it came to a choice between staying married to Philip and losing Peggy . . .' she shrugged. 'On the other hand, there's the TV thing, Isa won't give that up either.'

'And Philip doesn't fancy you any more?' Marcus grinned down at her satanically.

'No,' Anna shook her head. 'I'm beyond the pale—his mother said so. I'm a fallen woman.' She took a deep

breath and tried to match him for down-to-earth bluntness. 'Philip's mother would be looking at my firstborn
for a resemblance to you!'

Marcus gave her an encouraging hug. 'Oh, you doll—
you *are* coming out of your shell! But why worry? Your
firstborn, as you call it, will probably look like a ginger
kitten—I'll lay odds on that.'

Anna pulled herself together and headed for shallow
water before she went out of her depth. 'I'll send you a
photograph,' she promised blandly, and changed the
subject. 'Will Isa's being here make any difference to the
work? I think I ought to spare her a little time.'

'You can spare her your spare time, my sweet,'
Marcus said firmly. 'She invited herself here, so we don't
owe her anything. I hope she hurries up, Carl's ready to
serve lunch.' There was a finality about him and Anna
couldn't accept it.

'Isa's come here to me,' she objected. 'It's what she
always does when the going gets rough. She looks on me
as normality and a kind of refuge. I'm somebody with
whom she can be herself—I won't let you spoil it for her.'

He turned her in his arm and his finger came to raise
her chin, forcing her to look in his eyes. She held his gaze
for as long as she could, but there was something naked
looking at her and it hurt her to see it. She closed her
eyes, but it was no use—that damned attraction was at
work again, destroying her hard-held courage, making
her hot and wanting so that when he kissed her, her
response was automatic, almost eager. She felt tears
starting as she said goodbye to dreams of love—there
was nothing like that on his mouth or in his arms. Only
this awful wanting which dissolved her pride . . . She'd
never hold out for a year! She knew it and so did he!

'You mean she needs you to bolster her self-confidence,' Marcus spoke through the soft, warm mantle which surrounded them, a mantle shot through with starlight and moonbeams. 'You have to put her on the right track, make up her mind for her. That's not on, Anna, I've got a better use for you,' and she began to tremble. There was no way she could stop it, her mind didn't own her any more—all that was left was a silly, soft woman's body, and she was desperate to give it into his keeping.

'Aha!' Isa's crow of laughter broke the tableau and Anna felt the mantle slip from them, dispersing the starlight and every last moonbeam, and there was only the warm hardness of Marcus's arm and the sweet pain of her swollen lips to prove it had ever happened. 'A love-nest, after all!' Isa floated towards them, silk skirts swirling about her legs. 'What did I say?' she sounded pleased with herself. 'Anna, I never thought you'd be shy of telling me—I'm very broadminded.'

Anna stood rigid in a welter of guilt, incapable of stringing even the simplest sentence together—she could only think of one anyway, it went, 'I love you', but that couldn't be said. It would spoil everything. Marcus didn't want love, perhaps it was too cloying for his palate; so she left him to answer for both of them, knowing it would be something enigmatic.

'You see and you don't see, Isa—but lunch is ready, so let's go and eat. And while I think of it, you'll have to amuse yourself while you're here. Anna and I are wrapped up in our project and we've wasted enough time already today. After lunch, we shall shut ourselves away—You won't see a "Do not disturb" sign on the door, but take it from me, it's there. And tomorrow we shan't be here at all, we've got a little—er—research work which will take us away all day. By the way, does anybody know you've come here?' He kept his arm about Anna and she was grateful as he steered her in the direction of the *salon*. Without his support, she thought she might have collapsed in an undignified heap, and then there was his warm breath on her ear as he whispered,

'As my lady commands—no more alfresco meals. Carl is delighted. Like you, he's very conservative—almost a spoilsport.'

Isa followed them, her face puckered into a grimace. 'If you mean did I tell anybody, the answer's no. But there was a photographer and a reporter at the airport— I can't get away from them these days—and I'm almost sure they saw which gate I went through. We'll have to hope for the best; that no clever so-and-so puts two and two together . . .'

'I hope so as well,' there was an implied threat underlying Marcus's blandness, 'otherwise . . .' This time, the threat was out in the open and he left it hanging there like the sword of Damocles.

'Where are we going tomorrow?' Anna asked as he followed her into their workroom. It was quiet, and she scrambled herself behind the typewriter as though it would give her protection.

'Béziers first, then Carcassonne, if we can manage to get there before dark.' He looked at her speculatively. 'Will you scream or faint with horror if I tell you we'll probably have to spend the night there?'

This was a new Marcus and she found herself liking this version better. 'As long as it's not that old, hackneyed thing, you know—a loaf of bread beneath a bough, a flask of wine, a book of verse and thou beside me singing in the wilderness!' She smiled at the thought. 'I'll settle for a hotel room, though.'

'Single or double?'

'Single, of course,' she manufactured a very convincing smile. 'Repetition would bore you, I'm sure,' she pursed her mouth primly. 'You've done that once, so there'd be no novelty in a repeat performance.' And she swiftly changed the subject. 'I've got two versions of your first paragraph here and I've forgotten which is which, can you . . . ?'

Marcus scanned the neat lines of typing. 'This one, Anna. It has more impact, creates a better mind picture. "Neat, orderly rows of tents, vigilant sentries, all the order one would expect of an old soldier like de Montfort who controlled his band of cut-throats with an iron hand. His personal pennon—a silver lion with a forked tail, rampant on a red field, stirring in the warm wind from the Mediterranean . . ."'

'Warm wind from the Mediterranean!' Anna shook her head. 'That wasn't what I was taught at school. Simon de Monfort fought at Evesham, no Mediterranean wind would have reached him there. Never mind it stirring his pennon, it wouldn't have cooled his porridge!'

'Wrong de Montfort,' Marcus snorted at her ignorance. 'This is Simon the Elder, haven't you gathered that yet? You've read this first chapter often enough, haven't you? You've typed and retyped it at least three times.'

'I type,' she told him loftily. 'I don't read. It's all characters on the keyboard and one line at a time—like — O-n-e-space-l-i-n-e-space-a-t-space-a-space-t-i-m-efull stop. It'd slow me up if I had to *read* it!'

'Have you ever read anything I've written?' Marcus looked at her with almost horror.

'No.' She was on safe ground and could smile, even chuckle. 'Of course, I've seen your books on bookstalls, but . . .'

'But?'

'But I don't care for loads of violence and raw passion, which is what the blurbs say they're all about.' She wrinkled her nose fastidiously. 'I can't help thinking that novelists of your type exaggerate things deliberately for the impact value. I think . . .'

'. . . My dear girl,' Marcus interrupted, relaxed and drawling as though she was the favourite for the Stupid-ity Stakes, 'people, all people, are greedy, jealous and violent, they always have been—they always will be. Scratch anybody and you'll find a savage not very far beneath the surface. The human race has clawed its way to the top through rivers of blood. Dog eat dog! We've got a polite veneer of civilisation nowadays, but strip it away and you'll find a naked savage underneath. It's why we have laws—if everybody was truly civilised, we wouldn't need them.'

Anna rolled fresh paper into the machine with studied calm. 'End of lecture?'

'You don't believe me?' Marcus gave her a not very nice smile. 'Tomorrow, you shall learn for yourself. We'll go into Béziers and I'll give you a run-down on what happened there at the end of the thirteenth century and I'll explain why. It's time somebody stripped a few layers of smugness from you.'

'That's an insult!' she flared. 'I'm not smug, and you can strip all you want, you won't find a savage underneath, I'm not the savage type.'

'Everybody's the savage type,' he dismissed her statement as of no value. 'It's a matter of survival. The ones who survived were the ones who were willing to fight for what they wanted, and you're a descendant of survivors. It's bred in you from way back. You'll fight if you want something badly enough.'

It was a sweeping statement and it touched her on the raw. 'What do you know about fighting?' she demanded belligerently. 'I read what they wrote about you on the back of your books, and in my opinion, you've had it easy. If what they wrote was true, you were subsidised by well-to-do parents so you could sit in Paris and write a book. You didn't have to starve while you did it, scribble by candlelight because you couldn't pay the electric bill or huddle in your coat because you couldn't afford a fire. You can't call that fighting! And in any case, people should fight for others, not for themselves.'

'And you say you're not smug!' Marcus made a disgusted sound at the back of his throat. 'You're a typical woman with the typical, muddled mind. If you won't fight for what you want, it's not because you don't approve of fighting, it's because you're afraid you'll lose. But you'll never admit that, oh no! You'll think up every excuse in the calendar to do nothing and when you lose, you'll call it "Fate", or start convincing yourself either that you didn't really want it or that it wouldn't have been good for you to have it.'

'Put it in a book,' Anna snarled delicately, 'and stop lecturing me! I'm here to type, not to listen to your potty ideas. I thought we came in here to work . . .'

'That's right, use the old avoidance tactics,' he snarled back at her.

'I'm not avoiding anything,' she denied vigorously as he slammed down his pen and advanced on her desk to lean over it with both hands flat on the surface.

'You do nothing *but* avoid,' he accused. 'We haven't been talking about savages or civilisation, we've been talking about us, you and me, and you know it. I want you and you want me, I know that, so don't bother to deny it. But you—you have to hide behind your woolly little cloud of things which aren't "nice".'

'Things which are bad for me,' she corrected. 'We all have baser instincts and people spend a great deal of time and effort teaching us to control them before they control us.' Now she was quite calm; losing her temper, losing her control wouldn't help. 'Me, I'm controlling myself beautifully, I think; otherwise I'd throw the typewriter at you! How dare you even suggest a thing like that!'

'Because it's true, my little woolly-minded lamb.' He straighened up, grinning at her wolfishly, and strode off to the door where he paused with his hand on the knob. 'I'm going to have you, Anna. I've offered marriage and you've refused, so we'll have to manage without until you come to your senses.'

Anna looked up at him calmly. 'Not in Carcassonne, you won't, or if you do, it'll be over my dead body!'

Marcus only laughed. 'At the risk of sounding very coarse, my dear, it'll be over your very live body,' and he slipped through the narrow opening swiftly so that the paper punch which she hurled at him hit the door panels and fell to the ground with a thud, dislodging a spring and refusing to work thereafter.

# CHAPTER EIGHT

MARCUS was kind about his history lesson—kind in that he remained cold and factual all through their visit to Béziers and the small museum. He didn't make the sad little story live for her, and for that Anna was grateful. She had little stomach for senseless violence, and even the way Marcus told it, it was horrifying.

'I don't think I like your Simon.' The Mercedes was ambling along the fifty or so miles which separated Béziers from Carcassonne as if time was of no consequence, and Anna was consumed with guilt that she should be wasting so much time, time which she could have spent with Isa. But Marcus was in charge and, as he had pointed out bluntly, she wasn't a free agent. He was paying for her time.

'Our contract, Anna.' He had elevated it from a bargain to a contract. It sounded better, but it meant the same thing. It meant she had as little free will as a slave! She moved her shoulders irritably against the soft leather upholstery and went back to the massacre at Béziers.

'Killing innocent people just because they wanted to think for themselves and not accept everything the priests told them—it was inhuman!'

'Maybe, but in those days they weren't judged to be innocent.' Marcus was too disappointed in the scarcity of reliable records to be bothered about the massacre of the Cathars at Béziers. 'Heresy was a crime punishable by death, and the Cathars were an heretical sect.'

'But to burn them, when they'd taken refuge in the church,' she protested. 'And not only them but all the quite ordinary people who were trying to stay alive. No wonder I've never wanted to read your books, if that's the sort of thing you write about—I'll stick with Jane Austen! At least I can rely on her not to give me nightmares, and I'll be very glad when you've finished with the elder Simon. The one in England seems to have been quite a nice person—the champion of the under-privileged.'

'And died for it—fighting a weak, ineffectual king who always took the easy road.'

'A waste of a useful life . . .' Anna murmured, only to be interrupted.

'Nothing of the sort.' Marcus made it sound as though he was tired of discussing things with an idiot child. 'The man was a fighter, he believed in something, so he fought for it and later died for it. Not like you, Anna. You wouldn't lift your finger to get what you wanted. If what you want doesn't drop in your lap like a ripe plum, you pretend you didn't really want it after all.'

'Oh, stop criticising me!' she snapped, and half turned away from him to watch the scenery slipping past the side window. The sun shone like a great bronze platter, almost molten and making a heat mist shimmer over the road so that the macadam surface looked wet and the outlines of cars coming towards them flickered, seeming to be moving in the road and not on it. 'What has Carcassonne got to do with your book?

'Simon the Elder used it as a barracks on several occasions,' Marcus turned to grin at her. 'The old rascal was never friendly with the Count of Toulouse and it amused him to camp right under his nose.'

They reached Carcassonne just as the sun was setting and a rosy light outlined the old part of the town on one side of the river while the newer portion on the opposite bank already had dusky shadows creeping across it.

'Oh, lovely!' Anna pointed at the battlemented walls and turrets. 'It looks as though it's all been there for ever. It must have been very well built to look as good as this after hundreds of years.'

Marcus briskly stripped the romance from the scene. 'It wasn't any better built than other fortified places and it didn't stand the test of time. What you're looking at is a rebuild job. If you want to see true antiquity, I'll take you to Aigues Mortes. That's a fortification on the coast—past Frontignan. It was built during one of the Crusades—an embarcation point for the French Crusaders, but the sand silted up the port and it was never used. Over the years it was forgotten, and nowadays it's over a mile inland, but very much as it was when it was built. It didn't have to be restored, like Carcassonne, which was in ruins.'

'That's the kind of history I like,' Anna grinned. 'No blood! And I'd very much like to see it. As they say, it's education when you travel!'

'And I'm hungry!' Marcus was looking about for a parking space. 'We'll find a hotel, have a good meal, go for a walk along by the river, and then beddy-byes. Can I tempt you to join me? A double room always costs less than two singles.'

Anna was feeling happy, she didn't know why, but the happiness was there, bubbling up inside her so that she laughed. 'What a reason for seducing a lady!' she giggled as a silly thought struck her. '*Re*-seducing a lady,' she corrected herself. 'Is that possible? I mean—once you're seduced, can it be done again?'

Marcus found a car park at the back of a hotel by the river, pulled the car in smoothly and switched off the engine. 'It's always puzzled me, which one of us was the seduced and which the seducer.' He eyed her aggravatingly and as her mouth opened to give vent to a vigorous denial, he put a finger across her lips. 'But that's all water under the bridge, so don't let's start arguing about it now. I'll take the blame if it will keep you in a good humour and say that it wouldn't be easy to re-seduce you—you're an obstinate wench.'

'I'm fighting,' she reminded him. 'You said I wouldn't, but I am.'

'Why?'

'You ask that?' Her happiness drained away and she looked at him coldly. 'The fact that you had to ask why is sufficient reason. If you knew why, I wouldn't need to fight,' and she slipped out of the car, leaving him to work that one out—he didn't have the copyright on enigmatic sayings!

Several times during dinner, Marcus gave her an odd little look, but Anna met his eyes blandly and went on eating. The food was very good, although not as 'special' as the meal in Frontignan. The crème Vichyssoise slipped down her throat in an icy trickle, cooling her stomach after the heat of the day, but she suspected that the coq au vin had started life as a deep-frozen chicken. Marcus attempted to be lavish with the wine, but she shook her head and looked at him pityingly.

'You don't do that to me twice,' she murmured in deference to the other diners. 'It seems to make me either unconscious or quarrelsome, and tonight I've decided to be on my best behaviour.'

'Only twice?' He cocked a dark eyebrow. 'You aren't going to blame me for the first time?'

'No,' she felt herself blushing. 'The first time, I absolve you from blame. Then, it was all my own fault. That doesn't mean I've forgiven you for taking advantage of my condition, but,' she sighed ruefully, 'men will be men!' And she shook her head sadly.

'A Cointreau with your coffee,' he suggested. 'It's not alcoholic.'

Anna showed her teeth. 'I'm not that stupid. Isa likes it, so we always kept a bottle on the sideboard and I can read labels—it's something I learned when I first went to school. But if I don't have wine, I think I could allow myself a small Cointreau, it makes the coffee taste so much better.'

After a slow walk along by the river and an even slower walk back to the hotel—most of it in silence—they went up to their rooms, and at her door, Marcus kissed her. He did it with flair and enthusiasm and Anna responded likewise—but that was all. It was a definite wrench to tear herself away from him, go into her room and shut the door. She was shutting her loneliness in with her, but the pain of the wrench didn't keep her awake. After the shambles of the previous evening and the driving about in the heat of today, Anna was convinced that nothing could keep her awake. She would sleep through a full-scale revolution. Besides, in an odd sort of way, the long, quiet walk had soothed her and she had come to terms with her situation.

Marcus wanted her—she couldn't understand why, she wasn't his type, neither chic or sophisticated enough.

She'd refused, saying she wouldn't, and he'd said she
would sooner or later—almost like a sulky child who'd
been refused sweets. But Marcus wasn't the kind of man
who behaved like a sulky child. He wanted his own way,
but not because it was denied him. He merely assumed
he knew best, better than anybody else, what was good
for them.

And he seemed willing to wait it out—her mouth
curved into a faint smile—so could she wait it out!
Maybe she'd give in eventually, maybe he'd find the
password. It didn't matter. Perhaps some lovely lady
would enter his life and divert his thoughts—in which
case, she would have nothing to worry about except how
to mend a broken heart. The last time she had thought
she suffered from that, she had tried champagne, but the
cure had proved to be as phoney as the sickness. This
time, she'd be sensible!

'Did you sleep well?' Marcus glared at her across the
breakfast table the next morning.

'Like a baby.' Anna spared him a glance and poured
herself a cup of coffee. 'Did you?'

'You damn well know I didn't.' He pushed his own
cup across to be filled. 'How do you do it?'

'Do what?' Anna put on her most innocent air.

'Keep me awake half the night,' he shook his head in
mock sorrow. 'I lay there thinking about it and I can't see
any reason for it. It isn't as if you were Helen of Troy. I
suppose you know my book's going to suffer if I go on
like this.'

'Oh, the *book*!' She took a sip of scalding coffee and
squeezed experimentally at her brioche. It was warm
and very fresh and she split it and spread it with peach
jam. 'You mean I ought to climb into your bed because

you're writing a *book*? What a reason to produce, I'd
have thought you could think up something better than
that—and you a writer, a world-famous writer of
fiction!' The bright light of morning seemed to make it
easier to be acid and humorous both at the same time.

'You make it sound like taking an aspirin because you
have a headache,' she continued. 'My advice is—Calm
down. It'll go away if you don't think about it,' and she
took a bite at her well jammed brioche and a gulp of
coffee to wash it down. She thought she was doing very
well, the light touch, and the lighter the better.

'Dear Anna, you're a sadist,' murmured Marcus.
'Shall we, after we've looked around the fortified part,
go on to Aigues Mortes so that you can see what the real
thing looks like? It'll be quite a long drive and I'm sure
I'd be too tired to make the return journey to Agde. A
small hotel and you might be kinder tonight?'

'I shall be kind,' she assured him. 'Kind to Isa and
Carl. They'll both be missing us, so we'll go straight
home, if you don't mind.'

'That's a step in the right direction,' he approved. And
at her mystified look, 'You thinking of the villa as home.'

'Home's where the heart is,' she trilled with a saccharine smile, 'and my heart's with you all the time,
darling. Now,' she finished her coffee, wiped her lips and
changed her tone to one of strict practicality, 'shall we
get on with looking at Carcassonne, preferably the place
where all those tents were in neat rows, the sentries were
vigilant and the warm breeze was stirring Simon's
pennon.'

'You're scared!' Marcus sounded triumphant, and as
she bit her lip, his triumph grew. 'Oh, don't look like
that, as if it was something to be ashamed of, it's a

perfectly natural reaction. The Polar caps are melting in all this hot sun . . .'

'In that case,' she interrupted, 'I'd better get back to England without delay. But to change the subject . . .'

'I like this subject . . .'

'. . . And I'm changing it,' she said firmly. 'Would you like to give me a run-down on the next chapter in the saga of Isa and Philip?'

Marcus allowed himself to be diverted. 'I'm not sure, but if things happen as I think they will, if your Philip runs true to form, he'll be moving heaven and earth at this very moment, trying to find out where Isa has gone. That won't be easy, and if he fails, he'll start trying to unearth Peggy.'

'Oh no!' Anna's face whitened. 'Please, we must get back to the villa today—Isa must phone and see that Peggy's still safe. If Philip gets his hands on her, he'll take her to his mother and Isa will have to do what he says or they'll never let her see her child again. Philip's mother can be terrifying, she's so grimly single-minded.' She looked up at him, smiling wryly. 'Have you ever wished you'd cut your tongue out before you asked a question? Because this is one of those times. I'd rather Philip found Isa than Peggy.'

'Isa will have enough money to buy him off whatever he does,' Marcus pointed out cynically, and the cynicism took her breath away. Marcus seemed to think that money could cure anything—that a bottomless bank balance took the place of principles and moral justice.

'Why should Isa have to pay for what's rightly hers?' Anna demanded in a low, furious tone, and then a thought struck her. 'Besides, half that money's mine, and while I'd give every penny of it to Isa, I don't see why Philip should hog the lot.'

'He's her husband,' Marcus pointed out, but she wasn't satisfied.

'What you mean is, he married her,' she muttered angrily. 'That's all he did, marry her. He's never supported her and he's never contributed a penny to Peggy's upbringing. Lord, you men stick together, don't you! I've a damn good mind to get the next plane home, go down to Dorset and set fire to that house—and,' she added vehemently, 'I don't see why I shouldn't! It was *my* father's house and my grandfather's—I shouldn't feel in the least guilty about destroying it . . .'

'Arson is an offence punishable by a prison sentence,' Marcus's mouth twitched at her fervour. 'Don't be a fool, Anna. Why cut off your nose to spite your face?'

'To spite Philip's,' she corrected. 'He's turned out to be quite insufferable. He's a—a fortune-hunter! Only a couple of weeks ago he was mad because I was going to share with Isa—she was a bad wife and a bad mother, she didn't deserve. Now, according to Isa, I'm not to have a penny, it's me that's the wicked one now—no morals, hop into bed with anybody at the drop of a hat . . .'

'If only that was true!' Marcus sighed mournfully. 'Come along, my pet, let's look around old Carcassonne. I want it firmly fixed in my mind.' But as they left the hotel, he tucked a hand under her elbow and stopped her hurried steps.

'Are you sure this hate you've developed for Philip isn't an inverted love, a kind of jealousy? That you don't want to hurt him because he once hurt you?'

'Of all the . . .' Anna glared up at him and then cooled to an arctic temperature. 'That suggestion isn't worthy of an answer, not in words. It's the kind of remark that makes me want to bite!'

'Darlings!' Isa greeted them from the patio with a wave of her hand. 'Carl said you'd be back for lunch.' She was covered from head to foot in a floating chiffon pyjama suit and her face was hardly discernible beneath a wide-brimmed sunhat.

Marcus went off to consult with Carl and Anna joined her sister. She glanced around the sunny patio and her eyes lingered on the blue water in the pool before returning to Isa, whom she had expected to find prone and covered in a thin film of oil and little else. Her sister tanned swiftly and painlessly, going from cream to a deep, golden honey colour with no messy in between period of scorching pink; unlike herself.

'What's the matter?' Anna demanded. 'Have you suddenly developed an allergy to sunlight or to taking off your clothes?'

'Certainly not!' Isa huddled back beneath the canopy of the hammock-type swing she was using. 'Use your head, darling. This series is a period piece—the French Revolution—and I'm a high-born aristo—I can't have even the suspicion of a tan, it'll show up on film. It's a bind, but all in the cause of promoting Isa Carew to the dizzy heights of fame, so I bear with it. When it's over, when it's all in the can, I shall treat Peggy and me to a month in the Bahamas—until then, it's a cover-up job and I remain lily white, which, according to what I've read, was the fashionable shade for a lady of that time.' She looked at Anna sideways. 'And how did your little break go? Enjoy yourself?'

Anna flushed at the implied innuendo. 'Nothing like

that,' she muttered. 'I told you, I'm the secretary, that's as far as it goes.'

'Darling, stop blushing and drag yourself into the twentieth century!' Isa gave a little crow of laughter. 'You don't have to be coy with me!'

'Not being coy,' Anna's lips quivered. 'Isa, is that what everybody thinks? That Marcus and I . . . ?'

'I should think so.' Isa became strictly practical. 'And they're going to believe it, especially the women, because it's what they'd like to happen if one of them was in your shoes. I can't see you hanging out against an experienced charmer like our Marcus, and I know you, so it's a pound to a penny nobody else can. Besides, there are times when you look all lit up, an infallible sign. Relax and enjoy it, Anna, my sweet, it'll do you good. Stop being ashamed of yourself.'

'Ugh!' Anna shuddered. She had never been able to subscribe to Isa's. 'You only live once' philosophy; neither could she imagine herself going in for temporary affairs. Then she remembered why she had insisted on hurrying back and opened her mouth to ask if Isa had phoned to see if Peggy was still safely hidden, but she had missed her opportunity. Carl, morose as ever, was at her back intoning that lunch was served and Mr Marcus waiting, like Gabriel sounding off the trump of doom.

With a muttered, 'Wait for me, I won't be a moment', Anna fled to the cloakroom and gave her hands and face a cursory wash while Isa drifted elegantly off to the dining room.

Anna removed most of the signs of travel and smoothed her hair into some semblance of its normally controlled appearance, but it made her late. Marcus and Isa had already started on the soup, a clear, delicious minestrone, and her sister was meticulously picking out every tiny noodle. Anna slid into her seat to the accompaniment of a grunt from Marcus and the meal proceeded in silence until the dessert, when Marcus sat back in his chair, fastened his eyes on Isa, who was peeling a hothouse peach.

'Enjoying yourself?' he queried sardonically.

Isa didn't even look up. 'Terrifically.' She flicked a swift blue glance at Anna, one of encouragement as if to say, 'This is how you handle the Marcus Trents of the world. 'I hope I haven't put you two darlings out, and I do try not to intrude, but you've no idea what all this peace does for me. I was getting all up tight, the advance publicity has been rather nerve-racking.'

'Mmm.' Marcus nodded his thanks to Carl as the coffee tray was put on the table. 'That's one of the beauties of the place, peace—and Anna and I must have it, if we're going to do any work. It's important that I get this first chapter finished to my satisfaction, and I can't do that with a constant stream of visitors. You're quite sure that husband of yours doesn't know about this place? He can't track you here?'

'How could he, darling?' Isa looked mystified. 'We don't even know the same people. Oh, I know it'll probably have been all over the papers that I took a plane to Toulouse, but it won't mean a thing to Philip. Remember, you both skedaddled out of England at dead of night, shrouded in secrecy—at least, I never saw anything about it in the scandal sheets, so how could my moron of a husband possibly know about this place?'

Marcus shrugged. 'If you say so, but Anna's bothered in case he finds Peggy and does something foolish, like kidnapping her. Leaving her with friends isn't all that satisfactory—he's her father, he has the right to walk in and demand her, and if you're not there to stop him . . .'

'Grr!' Isa gave a mock shudder. 'Stop trying to frighten me, Marcus; I told you both, Peggy's well hidden. As a matter of fact, I think I was quite clever about that, almost inspired, and all on the spur of the moment.'

'Sometimes, Isa,' he remarked flatteningly, 'you tend to be a little too clever for your own good, and in your cleverness you rarely think of anything but your own convenience.'

Anna swallowed on wrath. She would dearly liked to have pointed out that the pot shouldn't call the kettle black. Marcus was a fine one to be reading Isa a lecture on consideration for others—when he never considered them himself! But losing her control and allowing a stream of viperish words to fall from her lips wouldn't mend matters, it might aggravate them, so she interrupted mildly,

'I'm sure Isa wouldn't be indiscreet, Marcus, and I don't think . . .'

'You don't think, period!' he snarled as he set down his cup with a bang that nearly cracked the saucer and scraped his chair back to rise. 'Come on, we've got work to do.'

Anna followed him out of the room, her face a white mask of distaste, but not a word escaped her until they were safely in the workroom where, as soon as the door closed behind him, she rounded on him fiercely.

'That settles it!' She stormed past him to her desk where she made a great deal of noise, rattling drawers in and out while she collected the few personal possessions she kept in them. 'As from now, you can do your own typing—and,' she scrabbled in her bag to withdraw her notebook, 'you can start by deciphering my shorthand notes. Nobody's going to speak to me like that, not and get away with it! Ha!' she felt herself fill with triumph. 'You hadn't thought about that, had you, Mr Know-it-all?'

'Thought about what?' Marcus was deceptively mild, but she was too intent on her own thoughts to notice, to beware.

'The difficulty of getting a typist in France.' She was riding high on a wave of triumph. 'English-speaking secretaries aren't exactly thick on the ground here—especially ones with a working knowledge of the vernacular. You'll be grounded, Mr Trent—up to your eyeballs in sheets of scribble, and serve you right!' She hefted the notebook in her hand, decided against it and chose instead a large piece of rock crystal she'd been using as a paperweight. It was satisfactorily heavy and she hurled it with all her might. It missed him by several inches and thudded into one of Carl's exquisite flower arrangements, which skidded off the side table and fell to the floor with a resounding crash, spattering blooms and water all over.

'Typical woman!' Marcus advanced on her. 'You couldn't hit a haystack at ten paces,' and as his arms closed about her, all the defiance and anger drained out of her.

'No, please,' she moaned. 'Don't . . .'

'Why?' It came as a husky whisper in her ear and then his hand was under her chin, forcing her face up.

'Because I'm frightened,' she admitted.

'Of me?'

Sadly, she shook her head. 'No, not of you—of myself.'

'You know it's going to happen.' He was quiet and serious without even a tinge of triumph and Anna was grateful for that understanding. He could have been aggresively male and tried to dominate.

'Maybe,' she admitted reluctantly. 'But I didn't want it this way. You'll never understand, we're too far apart in all the things that matter. I don't want to be ashamed of myself. Oh hell,' she wriggled in an excess of exasperation with herself, 'I don't even know what I *do* want!' But she did know. She wanted Marcus, but she wanted him to love her, not just for a couple of weeks or even a year. She wanted him as a permanent part of her life. Half measures wouldn't be enough and a temporary affair would turn to dust and ashes in her mouth. The thought of it made her very sad so that tears welled unbidden into her eyes and she sniffed inelegantly.

'Silly chit!' He raised a finger and brushed away a tear which was rolling down her cheek, and as she stiffened, 'Don't be scared, it's all part of the Marcus Trent seduction scene.' His mouth twisted into its old sardonic smile. 'I'm famed for it, I've brought it to a fine art, but I won't push you, my pet. Take your time—if anything's worth having, it's worth waiting for,' and the touch of his mouth on hers was as sweet as honey. There was no hard demand, no insistence, just a warmth and the feeling she'd had before of coming home. She bathed in it, gloried in it, and was almost imagining it was true, but there was a cold little part of her mind which rejected it. It was all a fake, a routine he trotted out to put her off her guard. The tenderness, the understanding wasn't real, it was counterfeit. If she gave in, what would she have? A brief, passionate thing which would wither as soon as it saw the light of day. She would be spoiled for any other relationship, going lonely through life and perpetually dreaming of him. She took a deep breath and pushed him away.

'Sorry,' she muttered with a travesty of a smile, 'I think I must be a bit tired. I don't usually throw things or dissolve into tears of self-pity. All the sun and the heat,' she babbled on, 'I'm not used to it, I think I've got a headache coming on—I'll get a cup of tea from Carl and perhaps he'll have an aspirin somewhere.' The words came out, thin and high, and she wasn't proud of the strained giggle which followed them but it was the best she could manage.

'One day,' Marcus regained possession of one of her hands and examined the fingers of it intently, 'one day, my girl, you'll learn to trust me. Go on, get your tea and your aspirin and have a lie-down. Work's finished for today and I shan't bother you any more, so you can feel perfectly safe. The next move has to come from you. Go on,' he gave her a little push towards the door. 'If you want me, I'll be out on the patio with Isa.'

'That's a good idea.' Anna was filled with disappointment and a strange sense of loss. 'She's much more accommodating than I am,' and she fled off to the kitchen to beg her tea, followed by his voice informing her that she was a tart-tongued, evil-minded bitch!

Carrying her tea and clutching a couple of aspirins, Anna went up to her room, her mind numb and incapable of reasoning. It was all too much for her, nothing she had ever experienced or read had taught her how to deal with a situation like this. What she'd read! She gave a little snort as she thought of her innocuous books.

Books from the local library where the librarian kept a vigilant eye on content so that anything either too bloody, too violent or too sexy was carefully put on one side and not on the shelves so that one had to know the title and the author and ask for it openly. So for her there had only been cosy love stories where the end, quite predictable, was always the 'happy ever after' type.

She swallowed her aspirins, washed them down with the rapidly cooling tea and stripped off to her bra and panties to scramble on to the bed and pull the light cover over her. This was where being too cocky had landed her, and she was amazed at her stupidity in thinking she could deal with somebody like Marcus. Her eyes were closing as she decided that what was needed was a diversion, preferably feminine and loaded with sex—Natasha would have filled the bill . . . The trouble was, Natasha wasn't here, and she was just bemoaning the fact and scheming how to produce a sexy diversion when she fell asleep.

'Marcus said you had a headache and you weren't to be disturbed.' Isa's voice woke her and she opened her eyes, blinking until her sister's face swam into focus. 'He also said it was all my fault,' Isa snorted. 'My fault indeed! I peeped into that room where you worked and saw the ruins. What did you do, throw the vase at him?'

'Certainly not!' Anna yawned. 'I never touched it.' She yawned again. 'What's the time, I forgot to wind my watch this morning.'

Isa examined her own. 'Half past six!' she marvelled. 'Time flies in this place—but never mind about that, Carl's putting dinner back an hour, the same as he put lunch back. That man's a treasure! Meals all higgledy-piggledy and not a cross word from him.' She flicked at

Anna's nose with a slim, very white finger, the nail lacquered a soft rose colour. 'Marcus was right, you've caught the sun a bit. I expect that's what made you feel groggy. Do you feel up to dinner or would you rather have something on a tray?'

It was a lovely thought, too lovely, and Anna dismissed it. She could not hide away from everybody just because she'd got herself into a fine old pickle. 'Of course I'm coming down,' she said firmly. 'Do you happen to have anything to tone down my nose?'

'The very thing.' Isa's little uncertainty vanished at such normal behaviour and she went off to fetch a pot of wonder-working gel.

# CHAPTER NINE

ANNA found the next two days extremely boring. She typed out her shorthand notes on both Béziers and Carcassonne and handed them over to Marcus, who grunted his thanks and inundated her with scrawled manuscript which she dutifully typed. She was on her guard, but he didn't make a single pass at her, not even one word that she couldn't have repeated to the most strict of maiden aunts. He was charming, in an offhand way, and after congratulating herself for sticking up for her ideals, Anna discovered that virtue was *not* its own reward—or if it was, she didn't care for it.

All the bite seemed to have gone out of life, she no longer had the exciting, dizzy feeling of walking on the edge of a precipice where one false word, one little slip would send her tumbling into a chasm where frightening, wonderful things lurked. Instead, she sat at her typewriter and for all the joy she had from it, she might as well have been back in the stuffy little office of Beresford and Blunt, making out Mrs Stott's will for the fifth time. Even a rise in pay didn't make it worthwhile.

Isa wasn't much company either. Carl had produced a set of 'Teach yourself French' tapes and her sister was immersed in them, playing them over and over in an attempt to improve her accent.

'It's important,' she dismissed Anna's grumbles about the constant repetition. 'I'm supposed to be French, I *have* to be able to speak it properly. Lord, Anna, haven't you read the book? Nearly three-quarters of the action's in France, ranging from a chateau in the Loire valley, through Paris during the Terror to a final escape after the fighting in the Vendée. Oh damn!' She looked at her watch and pulled a face. 'Marcus is taking me into Sête this afternoon and I'm not dressed yet. Be a pet and put away the tapes for me, I have to fly—you know how grumpy he gets when he's kept waiting.'

Anna watched her retreating figure and then busied herself with extracting the tape from the cassette player and restoring it to the box with its nine companions, and she jerked when Marcus spoke from behind her.

'I'm taking Isa into Sête to do some shopping, do you want to come?'

'No, thanks,' she closed the plastic lid with a snap. 'And don't come pussyfooting up behind me like that! Wear clogs so I can hear you coming.'

'And you'd better start taking something for those nerves of yours,' he advised. 'They're getting shot to pieces. You made seven mistakes on that last page you gave me. I've put it back on your desk for correction.'

'Which will give-me lots to do this afternoon,' she snapped irritably as she marched off to the typewriter.

He followed her, soft-footed in sneakers, so that as she reached the door he was right behind her and he put his arm across to bar her progress.

'What's gone wrong, Anna? I'm doing as you wish, not a word out of place.'

'Too much rich food,' she said tartly. 'It's upsetting my liver or something,' and then she ducked under his arm and went across to the desk where the offending sheet lay. '*Oooh!*' she squealed in temper. 'Did you have to decorate it with Biro? They're only tiny mistakes. I could have altered them. Now I'll have to do the whole thing again. Go away and make yourself fit to be seen!' She eyed his working garb, jeans, tee-shirt and sneakers, with disapproval. 'Isa prefers a well dressed escort even for shopping.'

'You are beginning to sound like a nagging wife,' Marcus reproved her with a glint in his eyes. She caught the gleam of it and after giving him a glare of pure frustration, she thumped down in her chair and started to interleave paper and carbons with fingers which were far from steady.

'Go away!' She rolled the paper into the machine, making a mess of it. 'You're putting a jinx on this typewriter,' she fulminated. 'I suppose you won't be back for lunch.'

'Depends on Isa and how long it takes her to find what she wants,' he shrugged. 'You know her better than I do, what's your guess?'

'I'll tell Carl to skip lunch,' she snapped savagely, 'not bother about tea and put dinner back by an hour, and I'd advise you to take a book or some knitting—In case Isa decides to have her hair done. Goodbye!'

This time the paper rolled in properly and she bent her head to give all her attention to her copy, hearing the soft thud of the door as he went out and then Isa's tempestuous entrance.

'Oh lord!' her fingers stilled on the keys. 'Can't you see I'm busy? You aren't going to the moon, you know. There's no need to bid me a fond farewell.'

Isa ignored the rattiness except for a mild concern. 'What's wrong, petal? Did you get out of bed on the wrong side?'

Anna said the first thing which came into her head.

'I'm worried about my dog—he could easily be missing me, and you know how temperamental he can be when his routine's upset.'

'Silly!' Isa gave her little tinkling laugh. 'Didn't I tell you? Your Alphonse will be having other things on his mind. Your vet's making arrangements for him to serve a couple of bitches while he's in the kennels, so you'll be on to a good thing if everything turns out well. A hundred guineas a time and he does all the work—that's what I call money for old rope! Alphonse will be enjoying himself, he'll probably never want to go home. See you later, darling, and don't work too hard while we're gone.' And there was only the slam of the door, the staccato rap of Isa's heels in the hall and a faint drift of her perfume in the silence of the house.

Another one enjoying himself! Anna punched the keyboard viciously. Everybody having a whale of a time except herself! She thought of a great many small articles which she could have asked Isa to buy for her, if she'd only thought about them in time—she thought about Marcus, sitting idly at some pavement café, whiling away the time until Isa emerged from the hairdresser's, and she made abortive plans to leave the villa for ever before they returned—go back home and live a dreary life with only Alphonse for company.

But she no longer had a home to go back to, only a load of furniture which she would have to store until she found somewhere to put it, and, ignoring the few sentences which she had already typed at the top of the page, she typed out a list of the furniture, a legacy from her mother and nothing to do with the house, and started a whittling down process. Storing furniture was an expensive business. It was all good stuff so the heavier pieces should command a reasonable price—she would only keep a few things.

Finally, she had reduced her list of 'keepables' to four—a davenport desk, a Sheraton chair, the bandy-legged footstool that matched the chair and a small carpet. She tried to be realistic about everything. It was going to cost Isa nearly every available penny to get free of Philip and to keep Peggy with her, so any hopes Anna had cherished about a small bungalow withered and died. There would be no nest egg for her and she would have to make her own way; even the old grandfather clock would have to go. It wasn't the sort of thing one could carry about from bedsit to bedsit.

Carl disturbed her, just before she became suicidal with a call to lunch, and she filled her head with specula-tion about how much she could expect from the sale of the furniture while she ate her way through iced melon, a soufflé omelette with a side salad and a generous helping of Carl's variation of Boodles' Orange Trifle, and then, worn out with mental exertion, she went upstairs in a defiant mood and flung herself on her bed. Marcus could wait for his typing—she didn't care any more.

The sound of the car returning woke her from an uneasy doze and she lay listening to the sound of the tyres crunching on the gravel. It was a real effort to hoist herself from the bed, her limbs felt as heavy as lead and every bit of her ached with the pain of suppressed tears. A bath would have been a nice, relaxing thing, but there was no time for it, so, stripping off and bundling her hair beneath a shower cap, she stood under ice-cold needle jets, trying to bring some life back into her sullen body.

A sundress in green cotton, spattered all over with white and yellow daisies and with a matching jacket, covered fresh underwear, and a pat with a powder puff and a smear of lipstick made her feel a little better. She gave her reflection a wry smile. 'Men have died and worms have eaten them, but not for love'. No, indeed! She wasn't such a poor thing that she'd die of not having Marcus—a week, a month at the outside and she'd have forgotten he ever existed—which was an encouraging thought if not strictly true. Anna pushed her feet into a pair of flat sandals and went downstairs to the patio, a bright smile of welcome pinned to her face. But it wasn't either Marcus or Isa who rose from the blue-cushioned chair to meet her, it was Philip, looking very much as she'd seen him last except that he had changed his riding breeches for a pair of not too narrow cords and he had left his spurs back home.

'Anna!' He sounded surprised and his pale blue eyes became a little more bulbous. 'That fellow,' he nodded towards the door into the house, 'he told me everybody was out, and I,' he added in a satisfied tone, 'I told him I'd plenty of time and I'd wait for you to come back.'

Anna seated herself and under cover of rearranging her dress, glanced at her watch. Half past three, and she reckoned she had about an hour in which to get rid of him—if she failed, he and Isa would have one of their hair-raising rows where Philip would repeat himself sturdily like a well trained parrot and Isa would throw anything that came to hand. And, in effect, Philip, *was* a well trained parrot, he reproduced his mother's dictums ad infinitum—'I'm an easygoing chap, but there are some things I won't stand for . . .'—'I'm a fair-minded man, but there are one or two things that get my goat . . .' An hour and a half wasn't long to deal with that sort of programming, but she would do her best.

'Hello, Philip,' she made it sound as welcoming as possible. 'Long time, no see,' and she let her extended hand drop to her side. Isa had been right. Philip had decided she, Anna, was contaminated and he wasn't going to touch her in case he or one of his cherished colts or fillies contracted a severe case of the staggers. 'Marcus isn't here, I'm afraid, and I'm not expecting him back for some time. Would you like a cup of tea before you start back?'

'I shall wait.' Philip was firm and heavy handed, like a shovelful of well set cement. 'I'll have some tea, I could do with it, but I'm not going till I've had a word with Isa.—Oh yes, I know she's here, the papers were full of it the day before yesterday: The glamorous Miss Isa Carew, flying out to join Marcus Trent at his villa near Agde. This sort of thing has got to stop!'

'What sort of thing?' Anna asked mildly, and her question wasn't sufficiently forceful to get through. Philip continued as though she'd never spoken.

'I'm not going to allow it, and Mother agrees with me. It's all right for Isa to do this film thing, but she has to realise that as a wife and a mother, her place is by my side . . .' Anna broke in on a louder note, determined that this time she wouldn't be ignored.

'Supporting you, Philip? Don't you mean propping you up?'

'She can do her bit of acting, I'll allow that.' Anna began to wonder if he was deaf or simply concentrating on the speeches he'd been practising and rehearsing during the journey.

'I don't think you could stop her,' she pointed out, 'and if the TV series is a success, her "bit of acting" could prove very lucrative.' She prided herself she knew Philip—he worked to a set pattern and his conversation followed the same lines. It was all thought out in advance, and once she managed to stop him, make him lose his place, he'd start to flounder and bluster. On the other hand, perhaps it might be better to let him go on, get it all off his chest, then, left with nothing more to say, he'd dry up like a stream in a hot summer.

'She's getting herself a bad name,' he trotted it out as though it was something novel. 'Everybody knows what the acting profession's like. Actors seem to believe they don't have to conform to ordinary, decent standards. It all started with those old Hollywood film stars—nothing less than licensed prostitution—four, five or more wives and husbands, changed as often as they changed their clothes. It's catching, and I'm not having my wife mix with people like that!'

Anna looked over his shoulder and fixed a sweet, grateful smile on her face as Carl appeared with a tea tray, and Philip took the hint and closed his mouth firmly, but his obstinate chin still jutted.

Carl set the tray down on a table and gave her a basilisk stare. 'If you want anything more, Miss Gentry, I shall be within call.' For one dizzy moment, she was tempted to say, 'Throw this gentleman out or toss him in the pool, whichever you wish', but she clamped down on herself; she'd caught some very bad habits from Marcus—his way of saying exactly what was in his mind was contagious.

Philip watched Carl's retreating back and accepted a cup of tea with a scowl. 'I don't like that fellow,' he gave his verdict. 'What is he, some sort of ex-bruiser?'

'Not at all,' Anna heard herself being chilly. 'Carl's a

treasure, I don't know what we'd do without him, and he's a very nice person. As a matter of fact,' she poured her own tea and sipped at it gratefully, 'he's much nicer than you are. Now, as regards Isa, I think you've left things a bit late, haven't you? She's already filed for divorce.'

'And I've applied for custody of Peggy.' Philip looked pleased with himself, as though he'd solved everything.

'Then there's nothing more to be said,' Anna said judiciously. 'And I think you've made a wasted journey, coming here. Drink your tea and go home, is my advice; think about it again. Isa can be a very uncomfortable person if she's upset. Be sensible and go, leave things to work themselves out,' but as she spoke, she knew she was wasting her time and breath, and Philip confirmed it.

'I'm waiting for her, if I have to stay here all night!'

'Marcus will be with her,' she warned quietly, but it was no use.

'So?' He shrugged his shoulders and raised a fair eyebrow. 'He doesn't scare me!'

'He could have you thrown out,' she pointed out. 'This is his house, you're on private property—and besides, you'd be wasting your time. Isa isn't going to call off the divorce.'

'She will, if she wants to keep Peggy,' Philip interrupted on a note of satisfaction, and Anna finally came to the end of her patience.

'You bastard!' she spat. 'Using a little girl to get your own way! Fighting over her like a dog over a bone! I could forgive you for that if you had one spark of affection for the child, but you haven't. To you, she's just a tool—and,' she hadn't mentioned money so far, she'd kept well away from the subject, but now it all spilled out, 'you don't really want Isa either—all you want is the money so you can set up your new stables. When you thought I had it, you were sniffing round me, but as soon as you discovered it was Isa's, you soon changed your tune. You don't want Isa and you don't want Peggy, and you wouldn't touch either of them if they didn't have a penny. You haven't a spark of affection for them—the only thing you care about is those damn horses and what your mummy tells you!'

'We'll leave my mother out of this,' Philip got on his high horse.

'Not when there's fifty thousand pounds at stake, you won't!' she shouted. 'Your mother wouldn't let you. Pass up an opportunity like that—you must be joking! Your mother is a human cash register, and you've got an outsize Oedipus complex. Look at you!' she stormed. 'Less than a month ago, you were saying *we* should be married, and you hadn't even the decency to wait for the divorce before you were proposing. You're nothing but an opportunist!'

'That'll be enough from you, Anna,' Philip said loftily. 'You keep out of my affairs from now on. I know you've encouraged Isa all these years, encouraged her to leave me, encouraged her to keep Peggy from me and from her grandmother, and I know why you've done it. Oh yes, I've had my eyes opened about you at last. You're spiteful, you've never forgotten that I chose Isa, you've never forgiven me for it, you've carried on your spite, wrecking our lives . . .'

'Wrecking your lives!' Anna noticed Carl in the doorway and waved him away; she didn't need help for this.

'You accuse me of that? Let me tell you, you puffed-up, pompous prig, I wouldn't have you if you came with a hundred-year guarantee! I got over my calf love for you a long time ago.'

'And you weren't very discreet about it,' he sneered. 'Oh yes, I told you I'd had my eyes opened about you. Your airs and graces, that prim exterior—you even had everybody believing in you, you had me believing, but it wasn't any of it true—you were the bad one, Anna, not Isa.'

'We aren't bad,' she defended, 'not either of us, that's just your unpleasant mind working overtime.'

'Isa maybe,' he retorted. 'I'll give her the benefit of the doubt, but you—you came out in your true colours when you went off with this Trent man. An old acquaintance, that's what you told me, but you forgot to mention how old and how close, but I found out! That motel on the Poole road—the landlady has a long memory! She remembers him perfectly, he was there the night Isa and I were married, and so were you, and he came down regularly afterwards, once a month for nearly six months. That's how much you thought of me! Your trouble is, you're man-mad. Mother suspected it all along—she said you were too good to be true, and she was right. It takes a woman to see these things. You're a tramp, Anna, a promiscuous little tart, and I'm only glad I found out before it was too late. I'd have married you and you'd have betrayed me with any man who took your fancy. You're his mistress, and what's more, you haven't any shame. The sooner I remove Isa from your influence, the better and after we're back together again, I don't want you coming round. If you try to see her or speak to her, I'll slam the door in your face. I won't have you corrupting her, and Mother says you'd be a bad influence on Peggy. You'll be thrown off my property.'

Anna heard a faint click and was conscious of a warm pool in her lap. She looked down and discovered she'd wrenched the handle from her teacup. The result of controlling her temper, she thought wryly. If she hadn't made such a good job of it, if she'd obeyed her instincts and thrown everything at Philip's smug face, she wouldn't have drenched herself with warm tea, but it wasn't too late, the tray was still there on the table and she would enjoy smashing every piece of fine china over his self-satisfied head. She wasn't normally a violent person, but there came a time when violence was the only thing that filled the bill.___

Without any hesitation, she launched the broken cup at him and followed it up with the milk jug, feeling a blissful triumph as the jug hit his shoulder and sent a spray of milk all over his tweed jacket. Milk was better than tea, if it wasn't cleaned off straight away, it stank! Her hand was just fondling the sugar basin and she had her eye on the teapot when she heard Isa's squeal and Marcus spoke from behind her.

'That's the best tea-set, Anna. It's for drinking from, not for throwing at,' he was gently reproving. 'What's going on here?'

'Get him out of my sight!' Anna muttered between lips rigid with anger.

'You heard the lady.' Marcus turned to Philip who was mopping himself up. 'She doesn't want to see you, so be a good, considerate fellow and go.'

'I didn't come all this way to see *her*,' Philip put a wealth of meaning into it. 'I came to see my wife.

Where's she gone? She was here a moment ago, I heard her.'

'I don't think Isa wants to see you either,' Marcus was deceptively bland as he detached the teapot from Anna's fingers and restored it to the tray. 'In fact, I don't think anybody here wants to see you. You're what the French call "*de trop*". As I came in,' he continued mildly, 'I heard you say something about throwing Anna off your property. Do you want me to throw you off mine?'

'I'm here to see Isa,' Philip insisted stubbornly, 'and I'm not leaving until I do. She's my wife and I've got the right . . . I've told Anna what I think of her and now I want to see Isa.'

'And what do you think of Anna?' Marcus put a hard arm about her waist. 'What does he think of you, my love?'

'The worst!' She fought to be free, but the arm wouldn't budge a fraction of an inch and she ceased struggling. 'Didn't you know?' she demanded in a thinly shrill voice. 'I'm man-mad, I'm a promiscuous tart, a tramp—I've no shame and,' at this point, her voice broke, 'I'm a bad influence as well!'

'And what have you done to deserve a reputation like that, my pet?' Marcus was treating it all as a joke, he didn't seem to be taking it seriously, and her temper rose again.

'I've consorted with you,' she spat. 'What else? That's enough to damn me in anybody's eyes.'

'You're ashamed of it?' They might have been alone on the patio for all the attention they paid to Philip, who was still voicing his wish to see Isa in a somewhat plaintive tone.

'No, I'm *not*,' she scolded, 'Do you think I care what

this stuffed shirt says about me, or what anybody says?' she added. 'I'm not ashamed of anything I've done, I'll stand in Trafalgar Square if you like and shout it all to the world. That's how ashamed I am!'

Philip was obviously becoming frustrated at being ignored. 'I demand to see my wife,' he repeated obstinately. 'I insist on it—there's the matter of the furniture. I don't want her doing something stupid before I get a chance to tell her.'

'What furniture?' Anna didn't have to ask the question, she knew what he was talking about.

'The stuff in her house, of course.' Philip found his wallet, selected a folded sheet of paper from one of the many compartments and practically waved it under her nose. 'I had the keys from the estate agent the other day and I went in and made an inventory of what we'd need for the new place on the Heath . . .'

'You needn't bother,' Anna snapped while she inwardly raged at this final humiliation. That Philip should have been creeping round, inspecting *her* furniture! Who did he think he was, God? 'You can make what plans you like,' her voice rose on a shrill stridency, 'but you won't get a thing, not a thing! Do you hear me? The furniture's mine, it has nothing to do with the house—it was my mother's and she left it to me. I'd burn every stick before I let you get away with anything there!'

'My dear Anna,' Philip was doing better than she was, he wasn't losing his temper—just being infernally smug and superior, 'you can't expect me to believe anything you tell me, and in any case, a thing like that would have to be proved. I daresay you've got round Isa to give it to you, but you're not getting away with it. That's another thing I'll have to speak to Isa about.'

Marcus threw him an unpleasant look over his shoulder. 'I'll deal with you later,' he promised nastily. 'Just now, I've got my hands full with more important matters.' He looked down at Anna and she caught her breath at the concern in his eyes. 'Go indoors, my dear, I'll finish up here.'

Anna gulped, aware for the first time that she was shaking all over. 'I don't think I can,' she muttered, a sorry little sound and lacking in any fight. Reaction was setting in and her teeth were beginning to chatter; she raised wide, frightened eyes to his. 'I don't think I'll make it, my legs have gone like cottonwool and it's suddenly a long way to the door. I don't feel v-very w-well.'

There were tears gathering in her eyes and she was ashamed of her weakness. Never before in her life had she felt like this; as though everything had drained out of her and she was as weak and brittle as a dry, hollow reed. The only part of her which was alive was her head, and that was beginning to ache abominably.

'You can make it,' Marcus insisted with what she thought was unfeeling cruelty.

'Maybe on my hands and knees,' she gave him a watery little grin, 'not a d-dignified exit.'

'On your two feet,' he remained unfeeling. 'Go on, you can do it,' and he released her arm and gave her a little push in the right direction. And she *did* make it; the flags of the patio heaved about like a ship in a high sea, but she didn't falter, not even when she heard Marcus's menacing snarl as he rounded on Philip.

'You stay here; you're not setting foot in any house of mine!'

Both Isa and Carl were waiting for her, and one on either side of her, they guided her steps up the stairs, although she protested all the way that she could manage for herself and that all she wanted was a bit of a rest.

'What I've been saying for days,' Isa broke in on Anna's futile muttering. 'You've been overdoing it, typing, tearing around the countryside in this heat and now coping with my soon-to-be-ex-husband. Who'd have expected *him* to turn up, the damn louse! It's no wonder you look like death warmed up. It's no use trying to reason with a man like that, Anna. He's solid bone from his forehead to the back of his neck.'

'You deserted me,' Anna complained wearily. 'You hid!' she accused.

Isa was busy with a cool sponge and then with un-zippering zips, and she didn't reply until Anna was completely undressed, reclothed in a clean nightie and tucked up in bed.

'I'm a coward,' she confessed. 'I'm only good at running away. At that, I've no equal. Besides, it's never any use trying to make Philip see reason, he doesn't know the meaning of the word. Now, you're going to have a nice cup of tea, a pill and then you're going to sleep. Marcus will have got rid of him by the time you wake up and everything will be back to normal.'

But things weren't normal when she woke. It was quite dark and the illuminated dial of her travel alarm said it was almost nine o'clock. Anna struggled up in bed and looked with amazement at stars twinkling through the filmy curtains which covered the unshuttered windows. There was a gnawing pain in her stomach which she identified as hunger and the house was incredibly silent. The thick walls and the sturdy, close-fitting doors cut out a lot of noise, but not this much.

She flopped back on her pillows and listened carefully.

No, no noise at all, it sounded as though she was alone in the villa. Marcus, she supposed, had taken Isa out to dinner, and the thought of his doing that made her mad. After all she'd gone through this afternoon, they'd left her alone, nobody had even bothered to bring her a sandwich. Marcus was probably disgusted with her—she had a vivid mental impression of herself as she must have looked on the patio that afternoon. In a filthy dress, white face contorted with rage and yelling like a fishwife—enough to disgust anybody!

Anna swung herself out of bed, stuffing her feet into floppy mules and huddling herself into a cotton kimono before she pattered along to Isa's bedroom. Perhaps Marcus hadn't taken Isa out, perhaps they were, at this very moment, enjoying a post-dinner chat—relaxing, well-fed, to discuss what to do with her, Anna. She could easily tell, all she needed was a quick look in Isa's wardrobe to see which outfit was missing and which evening slippers weren't in the line-up.

But Isa's wardrobe was empty. Anna stared in dismay at the row of empty hangers, then went swiftly across to the dressing table and started opening drawers. Like the wardrobe, they contained nothing at all, and Isa's extravagant make-up case wasn't in its usual position. There was no doubt about it, Isa had left. Anna felt a cold chill down her spine. Please, *not* with Philip! Although it would be quite likely for Marcus to suddenly tell her to get out, to go with her husband, especially if he'd become disgusted with both of them.

Hastily, she left the room and shuffled downstairs, heading for the kitchen where, she hoped, Carl would put her wise on the latest happenings.

That room was empty as well, the cooker, the dishwasher, the table, chairs and the modern units, all were spotless and shining, as though they'd just been delivered and had never been used, and of Carl there was no sign at all.

For a moment Anna gave way to blind terror, until she pulled herself together. Of course everybody hadn't walked out and left her with no passport and very little money—although she deserved it. Marcus, even at his worst, wouldn't do a thing like that. He'd have made some arrangements for her—all she had to do was wait until he and Carl came back from wherever they'd gone. Meanwhile, she was getting cold. The villa's thick walls kept the rooms cool during the day, and at night they released their heat to make the place warm and comfortable, but that was for people suitably dressed and a sheer nightie and a cotton kimono didn't constitute proper dressing. Anna shivered and headed for the *salon* where there was a super electric fire if the usual log one hadn't been lit.

She would sit by the fire for a little while, think things out, then she would raid the fridge for something to eat. There *had* to be something and surely Carl wouldn't object, not if she told him she was starving. Scrambled eggs on toast or an omelette—almost she turned back straight away, the thought of food was making her mouth water, but first things first, and that meant warming up the *salon* while she was preparing something to eat and she pushed open the door.

Marcus rose from where he was sitting by the fire, set aside the book he was reading and gave her a welcoming smile.

'Hello, Anna. Do you feel better after that long sleep?'

# CHAPTER TEN

'I THOUGHT you were out, you and Carl,' Anna explained breathily, and then, because it was foremost in her mind. 'Isa's gone. Did you know?'

'Mmm.' He held out a hand to her. 'Come by the fire and get warm, you must be frozen in that get-up,' and he kicked at the smouldering logs, sending a shower of sparks up the chimney and a cloud of grey, feathery ash into the hearth.

She looked at him uncertainly. Marcus was capable of anything and she still didn't trust him, not when it was a matter of his own convenience. 'You didn't send her off with Philip?'

'I was tempted to,' he looked grim. 'Flying into the safety of the house and leaving us to fight her battles for her—but circumstances didn't allow. Philip—er—fell into the pool.'

'Good!' Anna came nearer the fire and started brushing up the pile of ash. 'I hope he drowned. He can't swim, you know.'

'So I discovered when I had to fish him out. Lord, I thought everybody who lived that close to the sea would have been able to manage a few strokes, but he floundered about like a grampus.'

'You pulled him out? That's a pity!' she sighed. 'I hope you let him go down for the third time before you rescued him. How did he fall in? Did he trip or something?'

'No,' Marcus grinned devilishly, 'I pushed him.' He displayed a hand, the knuckles of which were rather puffy. 'I'm sorry, Anna, I know you don't like violence, except for throwing things, but it had to be done. The poor fellow was getting overheated.'

'. . . But don't you see?' she interrupted. 'Sending Isa off like that, it could make matters worse. If he catches up with her . . . supposing she books into the same hotel by mistake? Isa can't fight,' she explained gravely. 'She always runs away from anything unpleasant, and Philip's definitely unpleasant. If she meets him or he goes after her and she hasn't anywhere to hide, he'll bully her dreadfully until she does what he wants. He's applied for custody of Peggy, and I know she'll do anything, give him anything rather than let him have the kid. And I don't want her giving him our money, not after what he called me,' she added darkly, and then became mournful. 'Philip said I was spiteful, and he could very well be right. I don't feel very proud of myself, not at this moment. I'm simply keeping my fingers crossed that he and Isa don't bump into each other for a while.'

'Definitely not before they both arrive in London.' Marcus bent to light a spill from the fire with which he kindled the end of a cigar. 'That's where Isa's gone, safely under the wing of Carl. They should be arriving at Marseilles any moment now—I drove them both down to Sête, where Carl hired a car to drive them the rest of the way. I believe their flight takes off round about midnight.' He paused and looked at the glowing tip of the cigar intently. 'I hope you're a reasonable cook as far as making breakfasts and the odd lunch goes. We can have the rest of our meals out.'

'Carl isn't coming back?' The tiny tremor that shook

her wasn't fear, she thought it could very well be excitement. She could hear the blood beating in her ears, but she remained on her knees, her gaze fixed on the crackling logs, outwardly in control of herself.

'No,' his voice came from above her and she didn't look up. 'He has a few things to do for me in England, some arrangements to make. We shan't have time for much when we get back. Which reminds me, I've got a problem and I'd like your views. It's all practical, but there are some ethics involved.'

Her flicker of excitement died and she became composed. Marcus was trying to tell her something and he was being particularly devious about it—she flicked him a glance from beneath her lashes—or could it possibly be that he was shy? No, she didn't think so—shyness wasn't a part of the Marcus Trent she'd learned to know. But there was still so much about him she didn't know.

'Yes,' she said sedately, answering the question which he seemed to have asked a hundred years ago. 'I can manage breakfasts and lunches, although you'll have to bear with me while I find my way around the kitchen. I could even do the dinner if you're working and would rather not go out. It won't be up to Carl's standards, of course, but I can promise you won't suffer from malnutrition.' Her mind went bouncing off on another track. 'I still can't think how Philip knew Isa was here. He couldn't have had a clue beyond Toulouse—he didn't know about this place. I keep wondering how he made the connection; maybe it was sheer luck—that's supposed to favour fools and drunkards. Philip's not a lush, but as for the other . . .'

She heard Marcus lean back in his chair and looked away from the fire to glance at him, but his face, in the dim light of a small table lamp, gave nothing away. It wasn't hard or sardonic, only expressionless, and his eyes were hooded so that she had no clue from them either.

'I told him, of course.' He made it sound easy, as though getting information halfway across a continent was no problem.

'Sneaky!' Anna raised her eyebrows. 'What did you use, jungle drums?'

'The telephone.' Marcus relaxed visibly as though he'd been waiting for her, fearing she'd blow her top, yet fear wasn't part of Marcus either. 'Not a person-to-person call, me and Philip exchanging information, that wouldn't do,' he gave her a wry look. 'You'd have accused me of collaborating with him. I merely phoned my friend, the one who writes the gossip column. I asked him how it could be done and he came up with the answer.'

'You're deliberately dragging this out,' she accused.

'Maybe,' she thought she saw him smile. 'My friend didn't think Isa's arrival here was sufficiently newsworthy to get more than a couple of sentences in the national dailies, but,' he paused aggravatingly, 'he has a protégé, a youngster with promise who, wonder of wonders, works for your local rag, I can't remember the name. In that, I was assured, it would get the full treatment—a photograph, the lot with details—native news, you see—local girl gets to the top and so on. Don't look so disgusted, Anna—after all, it was your idea and I thought that was the way you wanted it. You *did* say you'd prefer Philip to find Isa rather than Peggy, and I was only making sure he would.'

'Very Machiavellian!' Her eyes twinkled. 'But you're

quite correct, I did say that; but I hardly expected you to take a chance remark seriously.' She retied the sash of her kimono and scrambled to her feet. 'I'll go and change before I start getting the food, I can hardly prance round the kitchen dressed like this.' Her exit was rather spoiled by the floppy mules, but in the circumstances, she thought it quite effective—a mixture of homeliness and dignity. Marcus called after her.

'Something light will do, it's nearly ten o'clock, so we'll call it a late supper.'

It hardly seemed worth while to dress up, but she did, if only to match Marcus's suave appearance and the beautiful fit of his velvet jacket, although when she arrived in the kitchen she covered the front of the bronzy green dress with a plasticised pinny. There was plenty of food in the fridge and the freezer was also well stocked, so she made up a meal with a cold, glazed chicken, some lettuce hearts and other salad stuff, opened a bottle of brandied peaches and whipped up some cream to serve with them.

'And was it your idea as well, to be out when Philip came looking for Isa?' she demanded, a forkful of succulent chicken poised to put in her mouth. 'The idea was for him to find Isa, not me! And, if you'd told me about it instead of being so secretive; I wouldn't have gone to so much trouble. Do you realise I spent nearly half an hour trying to get him to go before I lost my temper and offended him? That's the worst of Philip, he can't take telling. He takes the mildest criticism as a personal insult.'

'I said I didn't think he'd get here so quickly,' Marcus chided.

'With a fifty-thousand-pound impetus, Philip and a

great many other people can move at the speed of light,' she snapped. 'You underestimated him, and I had to sit and swallow his preaching and his mud-slinging!'

Marcus's lips twitched. 'You didn't look as though you were swallowing much when I came on the scene—china flying in all directions, and you weren't swallowing insults at all, you were spitting like a wildcat!'

'That was only the tail end of it,' Anna said grimly. 'You missed the best parts. He knows about that motel, you know; only, as usual, he's got most of it wrong. He said you were a regular visitor there—all in the cause of indulging our vile and depraved passions! What are you laughing at now?'

'You.' Marcus touched his lips with a napkin. 'Anybody less likely to be the victim of wild and depraved passions, I can't imagine. Your Philip's an appalling judge of character. But he was right about me going there regularly—I did, for a while. Partly because I was writing a book about the Pirates of Poole and the motel was a convenient place to stay—and partly because I was hoping to renew my acquaintance with a girl who had ginger hair and who sang suggestive songs. I thought she might come along one night.'

'You expected me to go back there?' Anna's eyes glowed like green jade. 'After what happened that night, I never wanted to see the place again! Living with the shame of the memory was bad enough, never mind revisiting the scene of the . . .' she had been going to say 'crime', but instead, substituted . . . 'happening.'

'But nothing "happened".' Marcus shook his head at her while he set his plate aside and started to ladle out small bowlsful of peaches. 'Unless you've been naughty since, you're in mint condition.'

'Nothing happened?' Anna snorted disbelievingly and abandoned her chicken half eaten. 'I woke up in a strange bed, beside a strange man, whom I remembered only vaguely. He thanked me for a novel experience! And you say nothing happened! What do you mean?' In her agitation, she had grasped a fork with trembling fingers and was drawing it across the table cloth, the prongs making tramlines that snagged at the linen weave. Marcus clamped his hand on her wrist, his fingers digging in, almost crushing the fine, slender bones beneath the skin and flesh.

'What I say!' He leaned closer to her and while not raising his voice, each word came clearly. 'Use your head, Anna. Do I look the type? Do you honestly think I'm that sort of man? Have I ever given you any reason to believe I'd take advantage of a girl who was sloshed to the gills?'

'*Yes?*' She felt his fingers loosen the pressure, and then the hold went and she nursed her bruised wrist. 'Yes, you have,' she muttered defiantly.

'You're talking about the night we dined in Frontignan,' he shook his head. 'No! I wasn't trying to seduce you, I was merely making a little, a very little love to you. Was that what stopped you, the memory of the motel?'

'A memory of something, never you mind what. As a matter of fact, I never remembered much about that night. The singing, of course, and I think I drank your whisky, but after that, nothing. Not until I woke in the morning. I was glad in a way, the morning was bad enough, I shudder to think . . .' Her lips quivered and her eyes widened as she looked at him. 'Apparently it wasn't as bad as I thought. What *did* happen?'

He shrugged. 'That night in the party room, or whatever they called the place, I thought you were a hired entertainer who was giving me the come-on. You looked old enough to know what you were doing,' he chuckled. 'That dress and your make-up put about ten years on your age and you seemed to be all right while you were singing, but when we went outside to go across to the motel chalets, you simply folded on me. You went out cold and, quite honestly, I didn't know what to do with you. I couldn't leave you where you folded, there are men about who aren't as particular as I am, so I took you to my room for safety. I put you to bed—you weren't wearing much under that dress and it all seemed to come off together—and then, because I was dog-tired, I climbed in beside you.'

'Fully intending to apologise to me in the morning, I suppose?' Anna was acid partly through disappointment and chagrin. Her wild night, the one high spot in her life, had turned out to be very tame.

'Fully intending to smack your backside,' he corrected with a grin. 'I mopped a lot of the muck off your face and found beneath it a very lovely young girl who should have known better than to behave like that. Then you dodged out while I was in the shower.'

'I was eighteen, nearly nineteen,' she disputed sulkily.

'And I was thirty-one and I knew my way about, which is more than could be said for you,' he pointed out. 'I went back to that motel again and again, as I said, it was a convenient place, but mostly I wanted to find you. I thought you might have been worried.'

'I was,' she admitted ruefully with a wry little smile. 'For weeks!' Somehow it was easy to talk to him, talk as she might have done to Isa. 'I was scared stiff I might be pregnant and there wasn't anybody I could go to. My parents were dead, so was Isa's mother, and Isa was away on her honeymoon. I made myself sick with worry, until I didn't have to worry about that any more. The relief was *enormous*! But why didn't you tell me all this when you came down with Isa?'

'You looked so guilty, I couldn't resist stringing you along.' Marcus pushed back his chair and rose. 'Let's get this cleared away, you stack the dishwasher while I make the coffee. Then we'll settle down by the fire and discuss the future.'

'I shan't ever forgive you,' Anna muttered when at last she dropped on to the hearthrug. 'You could have told me, but instead you kept on and on about it. You blackmailed me!'

'Yes,' he said without shame. 'I gave Isa that role, she was a cert for it anyway—I made up a little story about needing protection and you fell for it, and from there on, things started to snowball.'

'And now, having got rid of Isa and Carl, I suppose you're going into a big seduction scene.' She sounded calm about it, but inside, she was a mass of quivering nerves. He still hadn't said what she wanted to hear— she didn't suppose he ever would, and without that magic word 'love', it all seemed like a play where she was a cardboard character, pushed around by a script he'd written.

She loved him, it hurt her to admit it, even to herself, but it was the truth. She'd been starving for him, and that made the half loaf he seemed to be offering look like a feast, but it wasn't enough, not really, and her heart wept. She loved, but Marcus only wanted; the equation wasn't equal, and to make matters worse, she knew that once he started, she'd never be able to resist. The physical attraction was hard enough to cope with, but add love to it and she'd be like putty in his long fingers. Unconsciously, she moved a little further away from him, out of his reach, so that his touch couldn't sway her or deprive her of her last reserves of strength, and her little sigh was melancholy.

'You sound rather sad about it.' It would seem she hadn't moved far enough, because he reached out and pulled the pins from her hair which fell about her shoulders, a rosy curtain in the firelight. 'Anna,' his voice was a caress. 'You know it's going to happen one day—we both know it.'

She kept her face turned to the fireplace, grateful for the warmth on her face—the rest of her was a cold, shivering sickness. 'It's not as I imagined,' she said gravely. 'I don't feel happy about it.' And that was the understatement of the year!

'You'd prefer to be married first?'

At last she found the courage to look him in the face, her eyes wide and full of sadness. 'Would that make any difference, do you think?' He, his eyes, his mouth, every bit of him was promising her delight, but without love, his love, it was all wrong, and she burst into speech.

'No, I won't do it! It's not right, it's too much like a property deal—all forms, stamps and signatures and a notice saying "Sold, subject to contract". That's not the way it should be—There *must* be more to it than that. I'm being cheated, Marcus—where's the glamour, the stuff of dreams? With or without marriage, what you're offering isn't good enough. It's shoddy, there's something missing.' Her brows knitted into a worried frown. 'Are you, by any chance, teaching me another lesson? You needn't bother, because I think I've learned it. Tonight, there's not a drop of champagne, not even a mouthful of wine to addle my senses. What you're offering is counterfeit, and that's one thing I'd only accept when I know I can't have the real thing. If that ever happens, then counterfeit will have to do—it'll serve only if at last I'm sure there's nothing better for me. Remember what you said that night we came back from Frontignan? You said you "wanted" me. I'll never understand why, but you said it, and I believe you—but wanting's not enough—not for me. I'd keep remembering all those other women you've wanted and each morning I'd wake up wondering if this would be the day when you'd want somebody else.'

In one swift, easy movement, Marcus was out of his chair and beside her on the rug, his hands on her shoulders. 'What-the-hell-are-you-talking-about?' He emphasised every word with a shake, and the violence of it took away a lot of her sadness, gave her back some courage.

'Like Natasha.' Anna raised her chin defiantly. 'She told me if things had been different, you would have married—she asked me to give you back to her—straight out! I felt as though I was in the butcher's, haggling over a piece of meat! I think, if I'd been in a position to give you away, I'd have done it there and then.'

'Thank heaven you weren't!' Marcus gave a groan of relief. 'I'd better tell you about Natasha, hadn't I? She seems to be the main stumbling block to our under-standing each other—and we're going to understand each other if we have to stay up all night. Somehow or another I'm going to get some sense into that dumb little head of yours.'

It was an insult Anna couldn't take. He could call her plain, old-fashioned, bad-tempered—a lot of things— but dumb, never! 'You were patting her bottom,' she accused. 'Men don't . . .'

'Oh yes, they do,' he interrupted. 'Especially Natasha's, she expects it,' and then he became serious. 'Natasha, my dear, was a young man's dream. Yes, I admit she was my mistress, and it lasted just as long as it took me to realise I was being used—too long, really, but I was young, and since it was my first real love affair, I wasn't a quick learner. Her husband was rich, influential, quite a top figure in the French Diplomatic Service. He could give her most of the things she needed, but he was old, and I mean *old*! Natasha had needs he couldn't satisfy. I know that now, but I didn't know it then. I was a romantic young fool, I thought she'd give up wealth and position for what I could offer, which wasn't much— not enough anyway. So I finished my book in a welter of disillusion and came back to England where I attempted to cure what I thought was a broken heart. Actually, my heart hadn't been touched, only my pride, but while I was realising that, I made quite a name for myself as the "love them and leave them" type.'

'So I've heard,' Anna sniffed disparagingly. 'What then?'

'Then? Oh, then Natasha's husband died, he was nearly eighty and he had several children by a previous marriage, which meant that Natasha didn't inherit the fortune she'd been expecting—she lost a lot of her wealth, not all of it because her father left her a lot, several vineyards, a very nice little estate and a smallish fortune, most of which she used to keep up the life style to which she'd become accustomed. Now I'd hazard a guess she's scraping the bottom of the barrel. Anyway, she was looking for another marriage, and by this time I had enough to satisfy her, keep her in style, I had fame of a sort—something which she loves; she adores queening it at dinner parties full of notables, and,' a satirical smile lurked about his well cut mouth—'I had one other advantage over her other suitor—oh yes,' at her surprised look, 'Natasha covers her bets, she's not the sort of person to put all her eggs in one basket.'

'What advantage?'

'About fifteen years,' he chuckled, and then became serious. 'I declined the offer politely, so I expect she's settled for another old, rich man. She's not altogether to blame, you know; her parents made her first marriage for her when she was barely seventeen and she didn't have a chance to get her values right, but she's like a cat, she always lands on her feet.'

'Poor Natasha!' Anna felt an overwhelming sympathy for the woman. Marcus sensed it and gave her a little shake.

'Don't start feeling sorry for her.' He pulled her closer. 'Feel sorry for me! You lost me when you were talking about counterfeit.' There was no hurt in the fingers which stroked her hair back from her face and tucked it behind her ears. 'I'm not offering you false coin, my dearest. What we have is too good for that, and I've put a lot of hard work into getting you and into keeping you where I could make sure I'd never lose you again.'

Anna silenced him in the only way she could think of; she slid her arms about his neck and pulled his head down to hers. She didn't care about anything any longer, that he wouldn't say he loved her. With her eyes closed, her mouth found his blindly, and mere words didn't matter all that much, not when this tide of feeling was sweeping her away from reality and into a heaven where the touch of his hands made every nerve in her body scream for fulfilment. This was hers, and she would have it without bothering about the future—that might be bleak, but she'd have something to remember.

The fire spluttered as the last log fell into a shower of sparks, but she didn't hear it. Her body arched against Marcus's compulsively—she was behaving very badly and she didn't care about that either. All she knew was that he was hesitating and all she could think of was that she had to overcome that hesitation or die in the attempt. She moaned softly in the back of her throat, and then there was no more hesitation, only a wild peal of joy as if every bell in the world had rung out in triumph.

Anna woke to the clink of a spoon in a saucer and the sight of a sky, still the pale apricot gold of early morning. For a second she snuggled back down on the pillows. Life was wonderful—the teaspoon chinked again.

'Lazybones!' Marcus put the cup and saucer on the bedside table and seated himself on the edge of the bed while she looked at him, a swift, comprehensive glance that took in damp, slicked-back hair, a freshly shaven chin and towelling robe that left little to the imagination. He caught her at it and his frank gaze brought a swift blush to her cheeks as she remembered her abandoned behaviour. To cover an awkward moment, she looked round at unfamiliar furnishings.

'Your room?'

'Mmm,' he nodded. 'My room, my bed, my woman,' at which her blush deepened and she struggled not to be possessive—to let him go free if that was what he wanted. She was here, she'd walked into it willingly and with her eyes wide open—a cage of love, desire and passion, but *her* cage, she wouldn't demand he shared it with her. She pulled the sheet up to cover her bareness and kept it light.

'Why?' she demanded plaintively. 'Why do I get the idea this has all happened before?'

Marcus shook his head at her sorrowfully. 'You've got a bad memory, my darling. I told you last night, it hasn't happened before.' He bent his dark head to plant a swift kiss on her mouth. 'No!' as she ceased fiddling with the sheet and her hands went out to him. 'Later,' he said firmly 'Now's the time we discuss our future.'

'You mean we have one?'

'Oh yes! Stop tearing that sheet to tatters and drink your tea. You have to be all bright-eyed and bushy-tailed, we've got a lot to talk about.'

That brought another memory back to her mind. 'Your problem—the one you were on about last night—the practical one with the ethical overtones . . . ?'

'. . . And which you successfully demolished when you seduced me, my ginger-headed witch. I'll have you know I was going to be honourable—probably for the first time in my life!'

But Anna didn't want to talk, not about the future; she didn't want to know about it; especially about how long it might last. This fierce wonderful thing, she wanted to cradle the present in her hands, treat it gently, make it last for as long as possible. 'The problem, never mind whether it applies or not, I'd like to know what it was.'

'It definitely doesn't apply, not any longer.' Marcus gave a resigned sigh, but his eyes sparkled with wickedness. 'But you're not going to be satisfied, not until you know all the ins and outs, are you? What a life I'm going to have, explaining every last little detail to you!'

She put on an air of indifference and shrugged. 'If you don't like the idea,' she murmured, 'you know what you can do.'

'Not on your life!' Marcus told her promptly, and he looked down at her possessively. 'Let another man have that? Never while I have breath—that's mine!'

So it wasn't to be a fleeting thing—she began to feel a little more confident, but she still kept things light and airy. 'I knew it,' she snorted softly over her teacup. 'A chattel—that's my fate!'

'We'll be married on Saturday,' he announced, and when her mouth dropped open with surprise, he put a finger under her chin and closed it. 'I've arranged everything—for instance, Carl's seeing to the licence,' he peered at the bedside clock. 'In another four hours or so, he'll be on the phone to know if you've any special preference about where you'll be married. Don't look like that, Anna,' he reproved. 'After all, it's your wedding as well as mine, you ought to have some say in what goes on.'

'You can't get a licence,' she shook her head in bewilderment. Whatever she'd expected, it wasn't this. 'You have to know things.'

'All on your passport, and what wasn't there, Isa supplied—your father's name and profession—I didn't know he was a Navy man . . .' Anna swore, briefly and comprehensively, but he only laughed. 'So that's where you got your salty language!'

'You've done it again,' she raged, 'you've changed the subject. I want to know about that problem, so will you get on with it!'

'Mmm,' he removed her empty cup from her fingers. 'That's just in case you start throwing things,' and then, at her outraged expression, 'My problem? Only that rehearsals start next Monday morning. It doesn't leave much time for a honeymoon, and I was going to proposition you about that. Today's Tuesday, and I thought four days in France—even if we do have to spend two of them driving up to Calais—would be better than twenty-four hours at a hotel in Brighton or Bognor Regis. That's where the ethics came in, but you took the matter right out of my hands—you destroyed my opportunity to be noble. I was going to promise to be as a brother to you until Saturday morning, if you wanted it that way. I was going to show you my better side.'

'Your better side? You haven't got one,' she growled, but it was very half-hearted. 'Marcus, you make me so mad . . . I don't know why I love you, not when you only "want" me.'

' "Love" is an overworked word nowadays.' He picked up one of her hands and examined it intently. 'You hear people using it all the time and about the most trifling things—"I *love* Nureyev", "I *love* that dress",' his mimicry was exquisitely cruel. 'It's been debased, lost all its original meaning, so I don't use it any more. Anna, my dearest,' his hand closed around her fingers, squeezing remorselessly, 'I want you, I need you—and not just for today, a month or a year. I want you for the rest of our lives, because it won't be living without you. I want you by my side each day and in my arms every night. That's what I was going to tell you last night, and you would have had your choice about how we spent these four days. I wouldn't have coerced you if you'd wanted to wait till Saturday, but it's too late now, you know it is! I'll never let you go, not now. I lost you once, but this time there's no escape—you'll never get away from me again.'

Anna had listened in silence. He had said all the things she wanted to hear. She looked up at him expectantly and when he continued to regard her solemnly, she exploded.

'Marcus!' She nearly screamed with frustration as she wriggled her hand free and threw both her arms round his neck, pulling his head down to hers. 'If you won't say it, you won't! Forget I ever asked you to—and kiss me instead. Love me!'

'That's my girl,' he murmured approvingly. 'Remember how, when we were talking about one of the Simons, you said you weren't a fighter? But I knew, if you wanted something enough, you'd fight for it.' His chuckle was smothered against her breast. 'Later on, when they're old enough, I'm going to tell our kids that their mother seduced me!'